BR EQUIPMENT 2

Drawings from *Railnews*

Words and Drawings by David Gibbons

LONDON

IAN ALLAN LTD

Contents

First published 1990

ISBN 0 7110 1925 8

Published by Ian Allan Ltd, Shepperton, Surrey; and printed by Ian Allan Printing Ltd at their works at Coombelands in Runnymede, England

All photographs courtesy of British Rail unless otherwise credited

Front cover:
Class 91 for use on the East Coast main line. *B. J. Nicolle*

Back cover, top left:
A pair of Class 37s get to grips with a heavy steel train.

Back cover, top right:
Push-button operated sliding door on a Class 156 DMU.

Back cover, bottom left:
Class 319 EMU shoe beam and shoegear.

Previous page:
A Mk IV DVT for use on the East Coast main line.

Locomotives in Profile: BR Locomotive Fleet Update   4

How Diesel Locomotives Work   10

The Refurbished Class 37s   21

The Bournemouth Electrics   25

Class 317/2 and 318 AC Electric Multiple-Units   33

Trains for 'Thameslink': Class 319 Dual-Voltage EMUs   37

The Anglia Electrics: Class 321 Trains for Euston to Northampton, Cambridge and Southend Services   42

Enter the Class 89   46

New Power for the West Coast Main Line   50

'InterCity 225'   53

Pacers and Sprinters   60

Super Sprinter Class 155: The Longer Look   64

Super Sprinter Class 156   66

How Sprinters and Pacers Work   69

HSTs Go Electric   76

New Look for the West Coast: Driving Van Trailers for Push-Pull Working   79

The Foster Yeoman Class 59 Diesel Locomotive   82

The New Class 60 Heavy Freight Diesel Locomotive   90

InterCity's New Mk 4 Supercoaches   94

Locomotives in Profile: BR Locomotive Fleet Update

The last 10 years have seen major changes in BR's diesel and electric locomotive fleet and this chapter shows the locomotive classes currently in service.

Several well-known classes have now been withdrawn completely, including Classes 25 and 27, the famous English Electric Class 40, and the broadly similar but higher-powered Class 45 and 46 locomotives. This pruning process will continue as new locomotive builds become established in service, notably the Class 60 freight locomotives; the 100 locomotives to form this class will replace up to 240 older locomotives.

A total of five new diesel and electric locomotives are still on the drawing board, ensuring that the rich variety of types that has been so characteristic of the British locomotive scene will continue.

Horses for courses

Locomotive class numbers define the power rating and generally the higher the number, the higher the power output. Any sub-classes are shown with an oblique after the class number; for example, 47/7 is a 16-strong sub-class of Class 47, numbered 47701 to 47716, and fitted with time division multiplex (TDM) equipment for push-pull working.

Most BR locomotives are allocated to business sectors. Brake systems are normally dual (automatic air and vacuum operating both on the locomotive and the train). Locomotives also have a direct (or 'straight') air brake acting only when running light engine. Most ac electric locomotives have dynamic (rheostatic) electric braking in addition.

The dynamic brake converts the traction motors into generators, their output being fed to resistances. This generation process produces a retarding effect on the motor armatures which is transferred through the motor gears to the wheels, slowing the locomotive down. Current flowing through the resistances makes them hot; thus, the kinetic energy of the train is converted into heat.

An electric train supply (ETS) is available from an increasing number of locomotives, the equipment being fitted as part of life extension schemes on some classes. Each ETS locomotive has an ETS index showing how much power is available, and if individual vehicle indexes are added together the combined total must not exceed the locomotive's index. Some locomotives were once equipped with steam train heating boilers but all have now been isolated. Note that practically all ETS-fitted locomotives, although capable of a mixed traffic role, are usually reserved for passenger and some parcels workings. The fleet size for each class is the number in service as at 1 December 1989.

Class 08/0

Number in class: 472
Max speed: 15mph
Builder: BREL
Length: 29.25ft
Introduced: 1953-62
Height: 12.75ft
Diesel engine: EE6KT of 350bhp
Weight: 48-49 tons
Generator: EE
Brake type: dual*
Traction motors: 2×EE506
ETS: none
Tractive effort: 35,000lb
Fuel capacity: 668gal
Brake force: 19 tonnes
Route availability: 5

* Some air brake only. Three locomotives in sub-Class 08/9 — as 08/0 but with cut-down cabs.

Class 09

Details as for Class 08 except:
Number in class: 25
Max speed: 27mph
Tractive effort: 25,000lb
Brake type: dual

Class 31/1

Number in sub-class: 125
Max speed: 60mph
Builder: Brush
Length: 56.75ft
Introduced: 1957
Height: 12.6ft
Diesel engine: EE12SVT of 1,470hp
Weight: 107 tons
Generator: Brush TG160.48
Brake type: dual
Traction motors: 4×Brush TM73
Electric train supply: none
Tractive effort: 42,800lb
Min curve: 4.5 chains
Brake force: 49 tons
Route availability: 5
Fuel capacity: 530gal

Class 31/4

As sub-Class 31/1 except:
Number in sub-class: 66
Max speed: 90mph
Electric train supply: fitted — index 66
All refurbished and fitted with an auxiliary alternator to power auxiliaries and train supply.

Fig 1

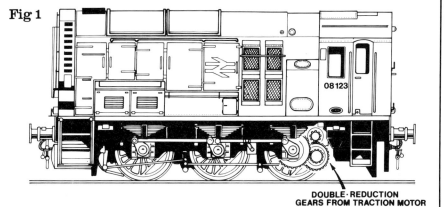

DOUBLE-REDUCTION
GEARS FROM TRACTION MOTOR

Left:
Class 08

Left:
Class 08 350hp diesel shunter.

Below:
Class 31 (unrefurbished condition)

Fig 2

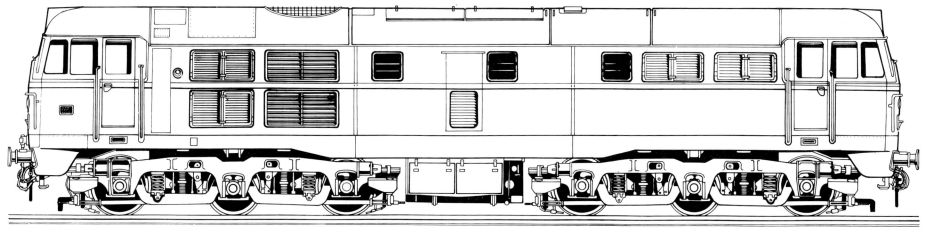

Right:
Class 37 (unrefurbished condition)

Fig 3

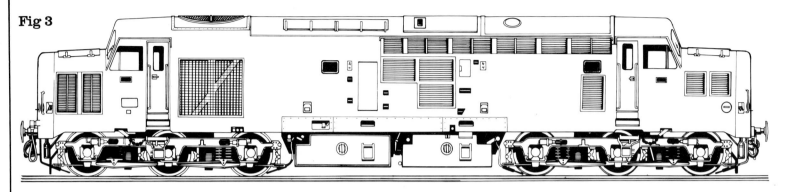

Class 37/0 and 37/3

Number in sub-class: 151 (*37/0*) 18 (*37/3*)
Max speed: 80mph
Builder: English Electric
Length: 61.5ft
Introduced: 1960 to 1965
Height: 12.75ft
Diesel engine: EE12CVST of 1,750hp
Weight: 102 tons
Generator: EE9115C
Brake type: dual
Traction motors: 6×EE538A
Electric train supply: none
Tractive effort: 55,500lb
Min curve: 4 chains
Brake force: 50 tonnes
Route availability: 5
Fuel: 1,689gal on some, others 890gal

Class 37/4

As sub-Class 37/0 except:
Number in class: 31
Electric train supply: fitted index 30
Weight: 107 tons
Fitted with Brush main and auxiliary alternators and rectifiers. All refurbished.

Class 37/5

As sub-Class 37/0 except:
Number in class: 54
Fuel capacity: 1,689gal
Fitted with Brush main and auxiliary alternators and rectifiers. All refurbished.

Class 37/7

As sub-Class 37/5 except fitted with ballast weights.
Number in sub-class: 44
Weight: 120 tonnes
Route availability: 7

Class 37/9

As sub-Class 37/7 except fitted with Mirrlees MB275T 1,800hp or GEC-Ruston RK270T 1,800hp diesel engines.
Number in class: 6

Class 47/0

Number in class: 125
Max service speed: 75mph
Builder: Brush/BREL Crewe
Length: 63.6ft
Introduced: 1962 to 1967
Height: 12.75ft
Diesel engine: Sulzer 12LDA28CW of 2,580hp
Weight: 111/112 tons
Generator: TG160.60 or TG172.52
Brake type: dual
Traction motors: 6×TM64.68
Electric train supply: none
Tractive effort: 62,000lb

Min curve: 4 chains
Brake force: 60 tonnes
Route availability: 6
Fuel capacity: 720gal

Class 47/3

As sub-Class 47/0 except:
Number in class: 79
Introduced: 1964 to 1965
Weight: 114 tons

Class 47/4

As sub-Class 47/0 except:
Number in class: 222
Max speed: 95mph
Electric train supply: fitted — index 66
Fitted with Brush auxiliary alternator for train supply and auxiliaries (except Nos 47401-20)
Fuel capacity: 1,295gal on some, others as 47/0
Tractive effort: 55,000lb (47401-20 only)

Fig 4

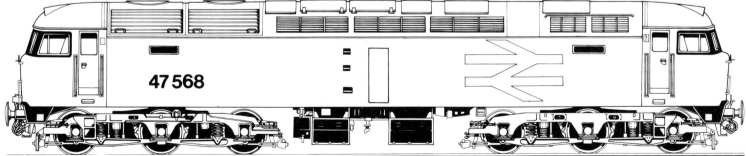

Right:
Class 47/4

Fig 5

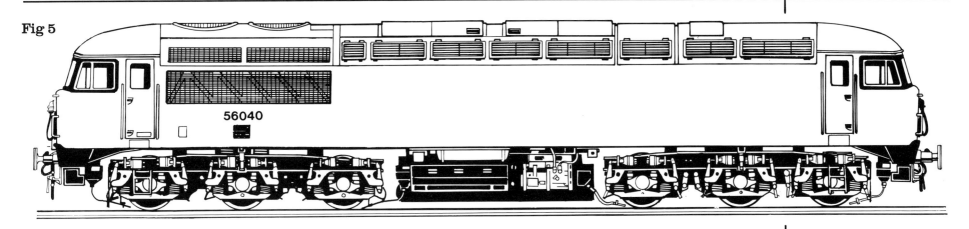

Fig 6

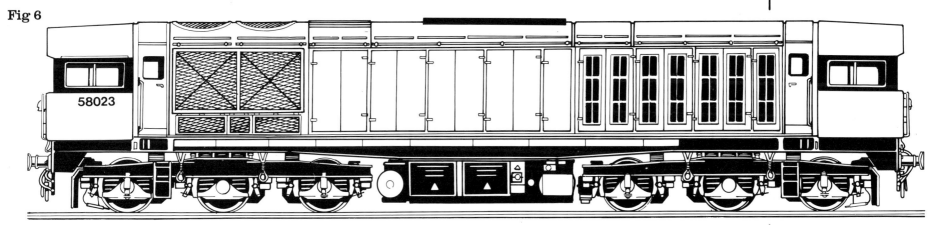

Class 47/7

As 47/7 except fitted with TDM equipment for push-pull working. All refurbished.
Number in class: 16
Max speed: 100mph
Fuel capacity: 1,295gal

Class 47/9

As sub-Class 47/0 except:
Number in class: 1
Diesel engine: Ruston-Paxman 12RK3CT V12 of 3,250hp
Tractive effort: 57,325lb
Brake type: air only
Fuel capacity: 1,010gal

Class 56

Number in class: 135
Max speed: 80mph
Builder: BREL*
Length: 63.5ft
Introduced: 1977-84
Height: 13ft
Diesel engine: GEC Ruston-Paxman 16-cylinder 16RK3CT of 3,250hp (some 2,400hp)
Weight: 126 tonnes
Alternators: Brush
Brake type: air only
Traction motors: Brush
Electric train supply: none
Tractive effort: 60,750lb
Fuel capacity: 1,150gal

Brake force: 60 tonnes
Route availability: 7

*The first 30 locomotives were built in Romania by Electroputere, Craiova (Nos 56001 to 56030).

Class 58

Number in class: 50
Max speed: 80mph
Builder: BREL
Length: 63.5ft
Introduced: 1983-86
Height: 13ft
Diesel engine: GEC Ruston-Paxman 12-cylinder 12RK3ACT of 3,300hp
Weight: 130 tonnes
Generator: Brush
Brake type: air only
Traction motors: Brush
Electric train supply: none
Tractive effort: 60,750lb
Brake force: 60 tonnes
Route availability: 7
Fuel capacity: 927gal

Locomotive No 56050 fitted with Brush separately-excited traction motors and wheel creep control for increased tractive effort.

Top:
Class 56

Above:
Class 58

Class 86/1

Max speed: 110mph
Number in class: 3
Builder: English Electric
Length: 58.5ft
Introduced: 1965-66
Height: 13.01ft
Horsepower: 5,000*
Weight: 87 tonnes
Brake type: dual
Traction motors: 4×GEC G412AZ
Electric train supply: fitted — index 66
Tractive effort: 58,000lb
Route availability: 6
Brake force: 40 tonnes

Fitted with driver/guard communication system.

Class 86/2

Details as sub-Class 86/1 except:
Number in class: 53
Max speed: some 110, most 100mph
Horsepower: 4,040
Traction motors: 4×AEI 282BZ
Fitted with SAB resilient wheels. A number are equipped with TDM equipment for push-pull or multiple working.
Weight: 85 tonnes

Some locomotives fitted with ballast weights, increasing the weight to 86 tonnes.

Class 86/4

Details as Class 86/1 except:
Number in class: 27
Max speed: 100mph
Horsepower: 3,600

Fitted with jumper cables for multiple working. This sub-class is expected to number only seven locomotives when the Class 86/6 conversion programme is completed.

Class 86/6

Details as sub-Class 86/4 but with lower traction motor gear ratios for working freight trains.
Number in class: 11
Max speed: 75mph
This sub-class is expected to number 31 locomotives on completion of the conversion programme.

Above:
Class 86/2 No 86242, the first of the class to be painted in InterCity livery.

Right:
Class 86/2 fitted with Stone Faiveley 100mph pantograph

Fig 7

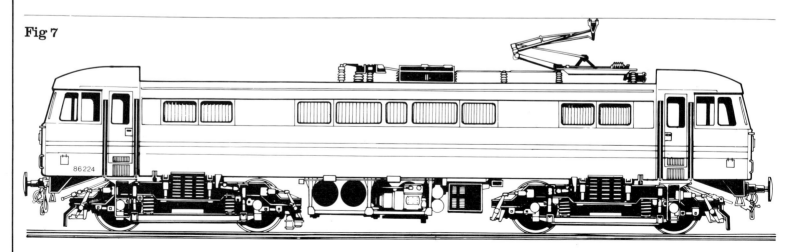

86 224

Fig 8

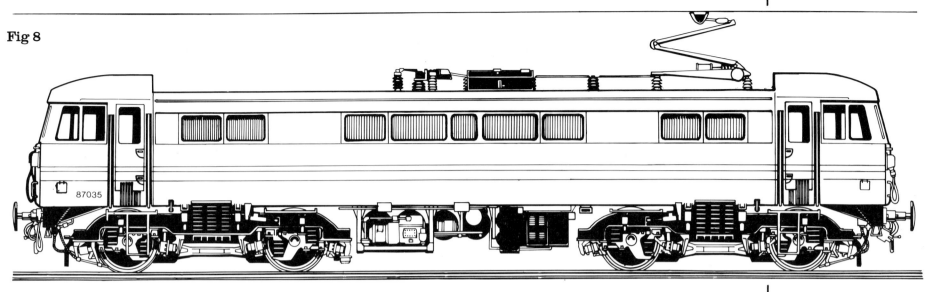

87035

Class 87/0

Number in class: 35
Max speed: 110mph
Builder: BREL
Length: 58.5ft
Introduced: 1973 to 1974
Height: 13.01ft
Horsepower: 5,100*
Weight: 83ft
Brake type: air only
Traction motors: 4×GEC G412AZ
Electric train supply: fitted — index 66
Tractive effort: 58,000lb
Route availability: 6
Brake force: 40 tonnes

Class 87/1

Details as sub-Class 87/0 except:
Introduced: 1975
Number in class: 1
Weight: 79 tonnes
Horsepower: 4,850*
Max speed: 75mph (formerly 100mph)
Traction motors: 4×GEC G412BZ

Fitted with GEC thyristor-based notchless power control system.

*Continuous rating

Above:
Class 87/0 fitted with Brecknell-Willis 110mph pantograph

Right:
Class 87 5,000hp ac electric locomotive.

How Diesel Locomotives Work

Introduction

The new Class 90 and 92 ac electric locomotives, the Class 442 'Wessex Electrics' and other new EMU trains have rightly focused attention on BR's electrified lines. At present, however, only 21% of the rail system is electrified (more when the East Coast main line scheme is completed) which leaves the bulk of the network powered by diesel locomotives and diesel multiple-unit trains (DMUs).

Diesel locomotives are literally the lifeblood of the system, keeping most of our coal-fired power stations alive by hauling several hundred merry-go-round (MGR) coal trains every week. In many urban areas, DMUs take thousands of commuters to work every day, and diesels keep the non-electrified portion of InterCity running, something easily overlooked by travellers in the densely-populated Southeast with their intensive EMU service.

Diesels are electric!

BR has possibly the largest fleet of diesel locomotives in the western world. The smallest main line locomotive is the Class 20 (Fig 9) with a single 1,000hp engine, while at the other end of the scale the Class 58 freight locomotive is powered by an engine of no less than 3,300hp.

All BR's main line diesels have what is termed electric transmission, which simply means that the power of the diesel engine driving the locomotive is converted into electrical power by a generator. This produces direct current (dc) which is fed by cables to traction motors and these drive the wheels through gears in a gearcase. Thus, the traction motors convert the electrical power of the generator back into mechanical power. The objective here is to control the tractive effort (pulling power) in a jerk-free manner without unnecessary complication. How these transmission elements are joined together is illustrated in simplified form in Fig 10.

Recent diesel-electric locomotive designs however, use brushless, low-maintenance alternators which produce three-phase alternating current (ac). This is passed to

Fig 10

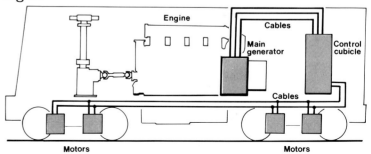

Right:
Electric transmission

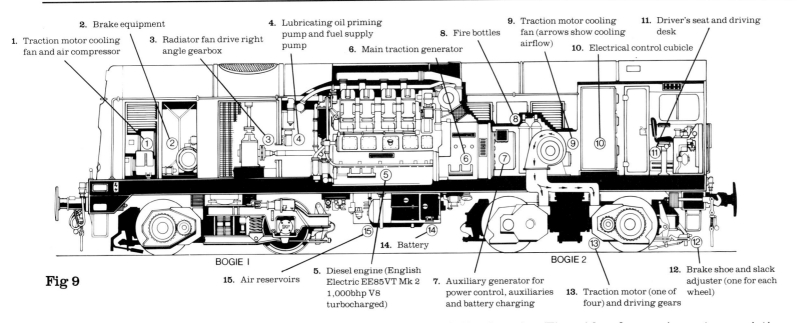

Fig 9

1. Traction motor cooling fan and air compressor
2. Brake equipment
3. Radiator fan drive right angle gearbox
4. Lubricating oil priming pump and fuel supply pump
5. Diesel engine (English Electric EE85VT Mk 2 1,000bhp V8 turbocharged)
6. Main traction generator
7. Auxiliary generator for power control, auxiliaries and battery charging
8. Fire bottles
9. Traction motor cooling fan (arrows show cooling airflow)
10. Electrical control cubicle
11. Driver's seat and driving desk
12. Brake shoe and slack adjuster (one for each wheel)
13. Traction motor (one of four) and driving gears
14. Battery
15. Air reservoirs

BOGIE I

BOGIE 2

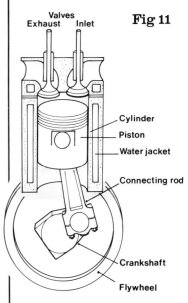

Fig 11

Above left:
Class 20 locomotive cut-away

Above:
The main parts of a diesel engine.

solid-state rectifiers to be converted to dc for the traction motors. Both the alternator and the generator are described later.

An alternative to electric transmission is the complex hydraulic system formerly used on some Western Region diesel locomotives. This was so named because hydraulic couplings of various types were incorporated in the design.

Two classes each had a single high speed diesel engine driving the locomotive's four axles via what was essentially an automatic gearbox with cardan shafts, Class 91 style, while two other designs using pairs of engines and transmissions also saw service. Eventually all four classes were withdrawn due to their high maintenance costs and the difficulty of producing an economic electric train supply for air-conditioned stock.

The diesel engine

The diesel-engined car is becoming an accepted part of the motoring scene, its longevity (some owners getting 150,000 miles-plus from one engine), low fuel consumption and sheer slogging ability making it an attractive alternative to its petrol-engined counterpart. It is these qualities (and lots more besides) which also makes the diesel first choice for rail traction.

A diesel engine (Fig 11) has four main parts, consisting of a cylinder, piston, connecting rod and a crankshaft. The cylinder is a short tube, closed at one end, and inside it a round piston slides up and down. The piston's movement from the top of the cylinder to the bottom is called the stroke.

The piston is connected by an integral gudgeon pin to a pivoting connecting rod which at its lower end is mounted on a crankpin fitted to a crankshaft. This is U-shaped with the connecting rod fitting into the middle of the U. If it is turned, the piston will go up and down. Conversely, if the piston is given a shove when it is at the top of its travel, the crankshaft itself will turn. The up and down (reciprocating) motion of the piston and the consequent rotary motion of the crankshaft is easier to visualise if the reader thinks of pedalling a cycle; the piston is represented by the knees, the connecting rod is the legs and the crankshaft is the pedals.

If air is admitted into the cylinder and the crankshaft is turned, the piston will move upwards compressing the air into a space only 1/25th of that which existed when the piston was at the bottom of its stroke. The air will now become superheated to a temperature of around 900°C. (An example of this kind of heating effect can be experienced

Fig 12

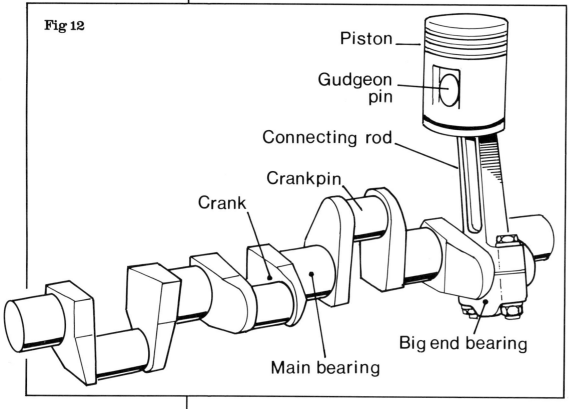

Piston

Gudgeon pin

Connecting rod

Crankpin

Crank

Big end bearing

Main bearing

with a bicycle pump; the last few strokes to inflate the tyre result in the pump barrel becoming uncomfortably hot.)

If, at this point, a tiny, measured quantity of oil is sprayed into the cylinder it will ignite immediately, burning up the oxygen in the air. This combustion will produce a rapidly expanding gas with a pressure of about 1,000lb/sq in that will push the piston down with an enormous force on what is called the power stroke, thereby turning the crankshaft via the connecting rod. A heavy flywheel fixed to the crankshaft will store this power impulse and use it to carry the crankshaft round so that the piston will move upwards again to repeat the cycle.

For this to happen, however, the engine needs a system of valves at the top of the cylinder to let the spent (exhaust) gas out and allow a fresh quantity of air to enter. These components can be seen on the drawing.

This is the basic operating principle. Part of a real crankshaft (Fig 12) shows how the pistons are fixed to the crankshaft — only one piston has been shown for clarity. The engine in a Class 08 shunter has six cylinders and six pistons while a Class 56 engine has 16 of each! Thus, with so many pistons acting on the crankshaft at different times, power delivery will be smooth and continuous.

The four operating stokes of the piston are shown in Fig 13. In the induction stroke (**1**) the crankshaft is being

Above:
Diesel engine crankshaft

Right:
The four-stroke cycle

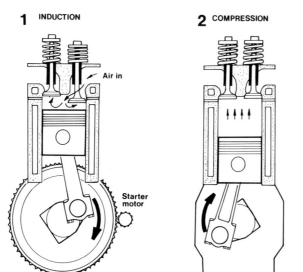

1 INDUCTION

Air in

Starter motor

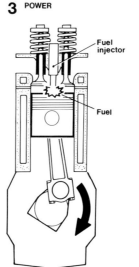

2 COMPRESSION

3 POWER

Fuel injector

Fuel

4 EXHAUST

Exhaust out

Fig 13

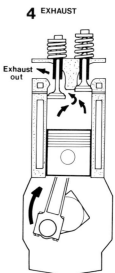

turned by an electric starter motor, moving the piston down and opening an inlet valve to let air into the cylinder.

Rotation of the crankshaft will continue, making the piston rise, the inlet valve will close, trapping the air in the cylinder on the compression stroke (**2**).

As the piston moves up to the limit of its stroke, the air will have become superheated, oil will be injected into the cylinder and the rapid combustion will produce a high pressure acting on the piston forcing it down on the power stroke (**3**).

The power stoke will now turn the crankshaft, the exhaust valve will open when the piston rises for the second time on its exhaust stroke (**4**) and the engine will now run unaided so long as fuel is supplied to it. The valves are closed by springs and opened by cams on a camshaft driven from the engine at half engine speed. The camshaft also operates the fuel injectors and it is so arranged and operated that it opens the valves and injectors at precisely the right time and allows them to close afterwards.

As the drawings have shown, there are four strokes in an operating cycle, a power stroke occurring every other revolution of the crankshaft. Engines to this design are said to operate on the four-stroke cycle, while the engines fitted to the General Motors Class 59 locomotives produce a power stroke on every revolution and have only two operating cycles, hence the term two stroke.

A diesel engine is known as a compression ignition engine for obvious reasons, making it different to a petrol engine which needs a spark to ignite a mixture of petrol and air fed to the engine by a carburettor or, in the case of some modern engines, a fuel injection system.

Both petrol and diesel engines are known as internal combustion engines and are quite different from a steam engine where combustion takes place outside the cylinders. BR's diesel engines come in many different shapes and sizes; Fig 14 shows the range of configurations.

The 12-cylinder Sulzer engine fitted to the Class 47s is in the double-bank category and is basically two six-cylinder engines placed side by side with their crankshafts linked by gears to a common output shaft. A far greater number of English Electric and the later GEC diesel engines are of the V-form type. Main line diesel engines are practically all turbocharged and intercooled, but more of this later.

Fig 14

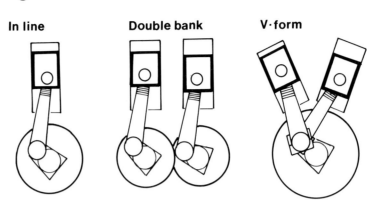

In line   Double bank   V·form

Keeping it oiled and watered

All BR's diesel engines are water cooled, the heat generated by combustion being carried away by water pumped through cooling passages called water jackets which surround the hottest parts of the engine. The heat in the water is dissipated through radiators, similar to those in a car, and cooled by dedicated radiator fans. These fans are electrically powered on some locomotives, while on others hydraulic motors are used. The Class 20 design, however, uses a direct mechanical drive from the engine to power the radiator fan (see Fig 9). Cooling water is also passed around the turbocharger and intercooler.

The engine is lubricated by oil under pressure, fed to oilways drilled in the engine block and inside the crankshaft connecting rods which take the oil to all the main bearing surfaces. Oil from the bearings, etc gravitates back to the oil sump below the crankshaft, where it is picked up by the pump and recirculated after passing through an oil cooler. Even the pistons are oil cooled on most designs. Unlike a car, however, the engine cannot be started until an electric oil pump has produced a flow of lubricating oil under pressure. The oil is water cooled to dissipate the heat absorbed from the engine.

Turbocharging

The word 'turbo' is usually to be seen adorning certain high performance road cars. Turbo has become a sort of 'buzzword' and is simply an abbreviation for 'turbocharger', which describes what is essentially a rotating device to obtain more power from an engine. What it does is very simple: it blows compressed air into the cylinders to increase its density so that more fuel can be burnt. Thus, the force acting on the pistons goes up and with it the power of the engine.

The turbocharger has two basic components: a turbine (a windmill) driven by the exhaust gas from the engine, and a compressor (a fan) rotated at high speed by the turbine, as shown in Fig 15.

Compressing the incoming air raises its temperature which lowers its density, so before the air is allowed to enter the engine cylinders it is water cooled by an intercooler. This extracts the unwanted heat and transfers it to the water, thereby restoring its density. The power to drive the turbine comes virtually free of charge from the heat energy in the exhaust gas.

Pistons, pumps and valves

Fig 17 shows some of the features of a diesel engine. Notice the lubricating oil sump in the crankcase below the crankshaft and the coolant spaces alongside the cylinder and the valves and fuel injector. The piston rings are like springs, pushing against the cylinder liner (shaded on the drawing), thereby sealing the combustion chamber above. Cylinder liners can be replaced relatively easily when they are worn: this is cheaper than replacing the whole cylinder block.

The fuel injector is supplied with fuel oil from a variable output jerk-type fuel pump, one for each cylinder, and operated by the same camshaft for the inlet and exhaust valves, as shown in Fig 18. The camshaft is turned by the crankshaft with a chain drive or via spur gears, and runs at

Fig 15

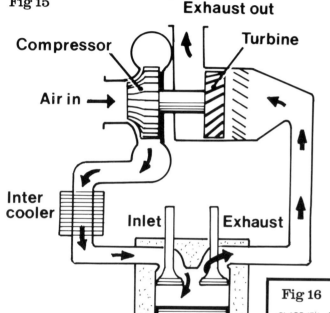

Left:
Turbocharging

Below:
Class 47/4 cut-away

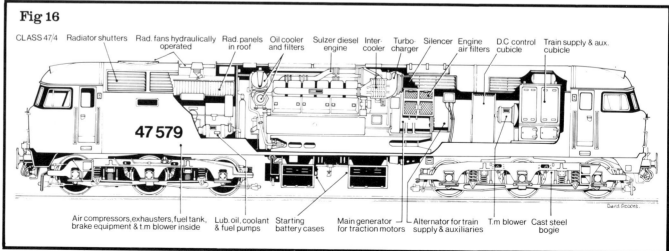

Fig 16

half the engine speed. It is usually to be found alongside the engine, running the length of the cylinder block and, on a six-cylinder engine, will have a total of 12 cams, six inlet and six exhaust. A single cam is pear-shaped with the fattest part integral with the camshaft. The slim end sticks out, forming a 'bump' and, as it turns, it lifts a cam follower which in turn acts on a pushrod and a rocker arm to open the appropriate valve against the tension of a spring. The spring will close the valve when the cam turns the 'bump' away from the cam follower. All the cams are arranged on the camshaft in such a way that they will open and close the various valves — or operate each fuel pump — at the right time in the four-stroke cycle.

There are normally two inlet and two exhaust valves for each cylinder. Rail traction diesels had four-valve cylinder heads years before high-performance petrol engines for GTI hatchback cars used them.

Power control

The power output of a petrol engine in a car is determined by how much petrol/air mixture is fed into the engine. This is in turn set by a 'throttle' (basically an adjustable air intake) operated by the accelerator pedal.

A diesel engine, however, does not have a throttle and draws the same quantity of air into the cylinders regardless of the engine speed. So, with a diesel engine it is the quantity of fuel injected which regulates speed and power.

The driver has two main controls: a master switch to set the direction of running and a power controller, usually notchless, which, on most diesels, is infinitely variable and sets engine speed. A diesel engine has to run within well-defined upper and lower speed limits, set by the engine speed governor to which the power controller is connected.

The governor controls the fuel pumps mechanically, their outputs being synchronised by a fuel control shaft running the length of the engine from which levers move integral fuel racks fitted to each pump.

Each cylinder fuel pump contains a small piston made to move up and down by a cam on the camshaft, thereby pumping the fuel to a fuel injector in the cylinder head. On a low power setting, the fuel rack turns each piston so that, as it operates, it spills more fuel back to the tank than it

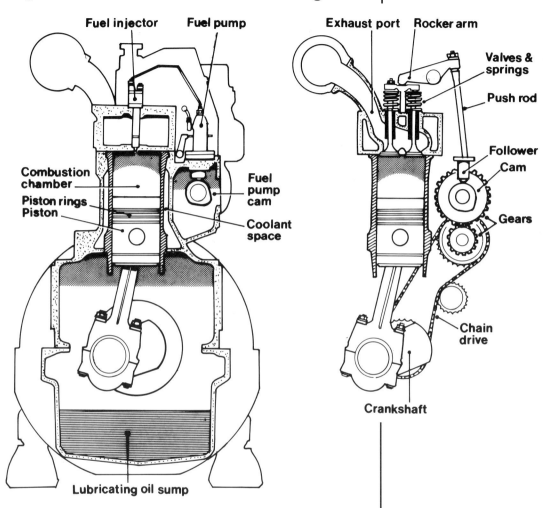

Fig 17 — Fuel injector, Fuel pump, Combustion chamber, Piston rings, Piston, Fuel pump cam, Coolant space, Lubricating oil sump

Fig 18 — Exhaust port, Rocker arm, Valves & springs, Push rod, Follower, Cam, Gears, Chain drive, Crankshaft

delivers to the injector. To increase the fuel output, the rack turns the piston to a position where the process is reversed and now the piston delivers more fuel to the injector than it spills to the tank. In this way, the amount of fuel injected into the engine is infinitely variable, from idling to full power.

Controlling the fuel rate is only part of the story and the governor also has to relate to the main generator/alternator in order to adjust their output in kW to match its equivalent

Left:
Features of a diesel engine.

Above:
Arrangement for working inlet/exhaust valves.

Right:
The fuel system

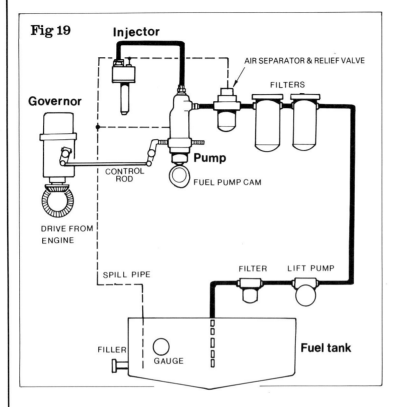

Fig 19

Injector

AIR SEPARATOR & RELIEF VALVE

FILTERS

Governor

CONTROL ROD

Pump

FUEL PUMP CAM

DRIVE FROM ENGINE

SPILL PIPE

FILTER

LIFT PUMP

FILLER

GAUGE

Fuel tank

lever is able to move independently to provide the overspeed feature. As the power controller is opened the eccentric moves to the right, carrying the floating lever with it, and making the control rod move towards the maximum fuel position, thereby raising engine speed, or vice versa.

The shaft and the eccentric can be power-operated under remote control by air, or engine lubricating oil, acting on a piston, thereby providing control of two or more locomotives in multiple from a single driving cab. Cables for multiple-unit operation are fitted at the ends of most diesel locomotives, plus an air hose for engine speed control where this is pneumatically operated.

As mentioned, the governor illustrated here is based on DMU practice. Its principle of operation, however, is embodied in the more complex locomotive governor designs. Most locomotive engines are also fitted with a second, overspeed sensing, mechanical governor arranged

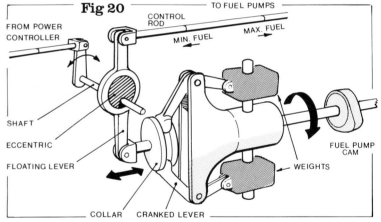

Fig 20

TO FUEL PUMPS

FROM POWER CONTROLLER

CONTROL ROD

MIN. FUEL

MAX. FUEL

SHAFT

ECCENTRIC

FLOATING LEVER

FUEL PUMP CAM

WEIGHTS

COLLAR   CRANKED LEVER

in horsepower delivered to the alternator or generator by the diesel engine.

Fig 19 shows a typical fuel system. The lift pump acts as a priming pump for the individual cylinder fuel pumps and is electrically operated.

A simple engine-driven engine speed governor from a first-generation DMU engine is depicted in Fig 20. It is formed of an extension of the fuel pump camshaft carrying a sleeve with projecting cranked levers on which a pair of weights are mounted, and these will move outwards by centrifugal force when the engine is running. Movement of the weights is transferred to the pump control rod by a grooved collar. Thus, if the engine overspeeds (Fig 21), the weights will fly outwards sufficiently to move the control rod back to the minimum fuel position, making the engine idle.

The rod from the driver's power controller will operate a shaft linked to an eccentric, around which the floating

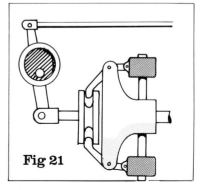

Fig 21

Above:
Engine speed governor.

Left:
Governor after overspeeding.

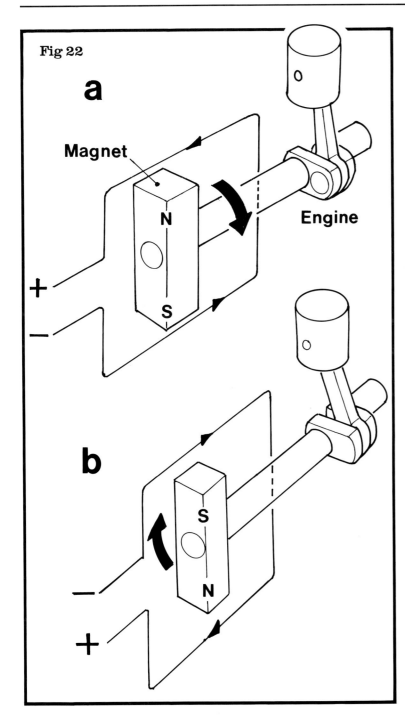

Fig 22

a

Magnet

N

S

+

−

Engine

b

S

N

−

+

to close the fuel racks on the fuel pumps automatically if the engine speed rises above the maximum permitted.

The control of the maximum speed of a diesel engine is vitally important — a diesel engine left to its own devices would simply run faster and faster to its own destruction.

Alternators and generators

It is easiest to understand the differences between an alternator and a generator by going back to basics. Starting with the alternator, most people will remember their experiments at school with a rotating bar magnet that will produce a current in a loop of wire, as in the elementary alternator in Fig 22a. The current will reverse direction every half a revolution of the magnet as in Fig 22b, and sharp-eyed readers will notice that the north pole of the magnet under the top of the wire in Fig 22a has been replaced by the south pole in Fig 22b. So, the current direction continually changes (alternates) in step with the succession of magnetic north and south poles passing the wire loop. The mains alternating current supply does this 50 times (or cycles) every second.

Like the bicycle dynamo, the alternator will produce an output that rises with speed. This output can also be varied alternately as shown in Fig 23. The rotating magnet has been replaced by a rotating electromagnet (basically a coil

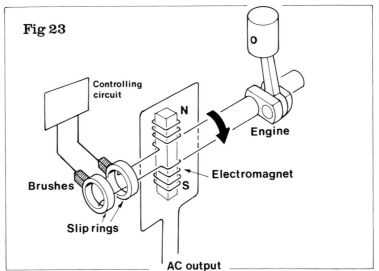

Fig 23

Controlling circuit

N

S

Engine

Electromagnet

Brushes

Slip rings

AC output

Left:
An elementary alternator

Left:
Alternator controller.

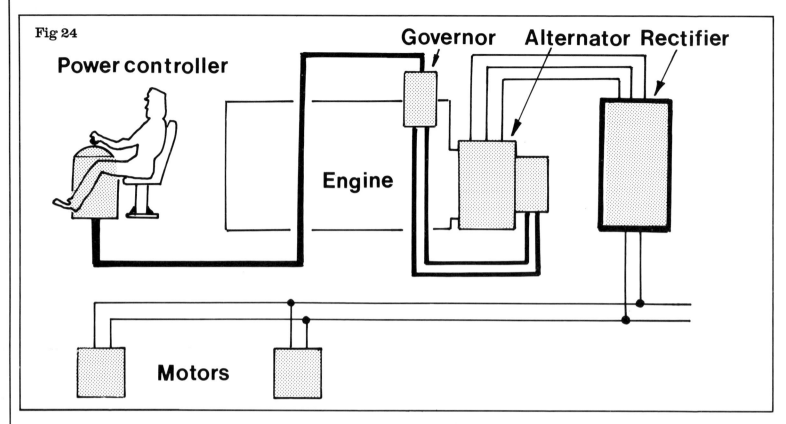

Fig 24

Governor   Alternator Rectifier

Power controller

Engine

Motors

of insulated wire wound around a soft iron core) and fed with current from a controlling circuit via copper slip rings which rotate with the electromagnet, and stationary graphite brushes.

The power of a magnet is fixed; an electromagnet can be made stronger or weaker by varying the current strength. So, if the current passing through the rotating electromagnet is varied and the engine speed is also varied, it is possible to control the ac induced in the wire loop.

A full-sized alternator is more complicated, with numerous coils both on the rotating electromagnets (the rotor) and the stationary field coils (the stator). They are usually brushless, with no moving, current-collecting parts. This takes a bit of explaining, so the alternator used here to show the principles involved.

In Fig 24 the basic power control system for a locomotive with an alternator is illustrated. The power controller

signals to the governor for more power which responds by raising engine speed while an electronic load regulator increases the current to the rotor which in turn increases the current induced in the stationary stator. The ac output is converted into dc by the solid-state rectifier before being fed to the traction motors. Only two of the four motors have been shown.

If the locomotive has its load reduced and less power is needed (when running downhill, for example) this is automatically sensed by the load regulator which then reduces the current to the rotor and simultaneously signals to the governor to adjust the fuel supply to the engine to suit the lower demand. This reduces the power of the engine to match the reduced power demand from the alternator.

All BR's recent diesel locomotives use main traction alternators, including the Classes 56, 58 and 59, and

Class 43 IC125 power cars. Other locomotives have hybrid systems like some converted members of Classes 31, 37 and 47. These have alternators for the train supply and auxiliaries and conventional dc generators to power the dc traction motors.

A very basic dc generator (Fig 25) is like an alternator and has the same parts, although their roles are reversed. The electromagnet (a field coil) is stationary while the wire loop is now a rotating armature in which ac is induced to flow. The clever bit is the rotating commutator, divided into two insulated segments and connected to the armature loop. The commutator acts like a rotating, automatic reversing switch that changes the connections between the armature, the current collecting brushes and the external circuit to the lamp each time the current direction in the armature changes.

Fig 26

a 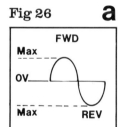   **b** 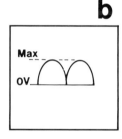   **c**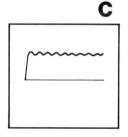

In this way, ac (Fig 26a) is 'converted' by the commutator into dc, as in Fig 26b. Finally, in Fig 26c, the smoother output from a real generator has been shown, with fewer peaks and troughs from a large number of wire loops (coils of wire) in the armature, each connected to a bigger commutator with more segments.

The real generator also has more than one field coil, and their strength is varied (Fig 25) using a resistance-based electromechanical load regulator linked to the engine governor. Engine speed and field strength vary the generator's output similarly to the ac scheme already described.

Motors

A generator can become an electric motor if it is fed with current, and its power is directly proportional to the current flowing through it. As it speeds up, less tractive

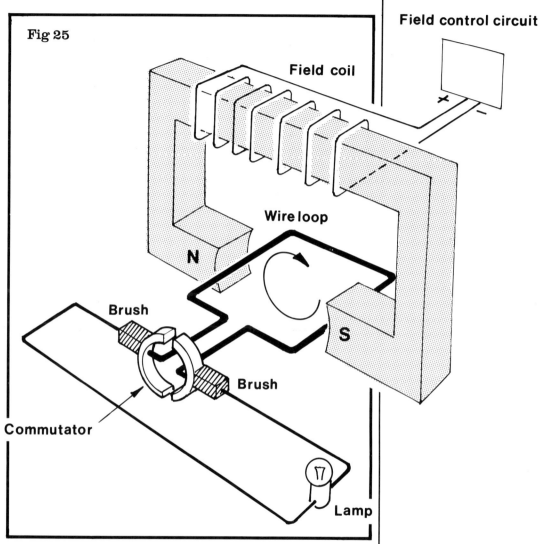

effort (and less current) is needed, a situation caused by the motor acting like a generator and producing a voltage of its own, called a back electromotive force (emf) which opposes the applied voltage.

Thus the voltage increases as speed rises, and to make it speed up still further its field coils are deliberately weakened to reduce the back emf. This process, called field weakening, takes place automatically on a full-sized locomotive. When the locomotive slows down on a gradient,

Above:
A basic dc generator.

Left:
Conversion of ac to dc.

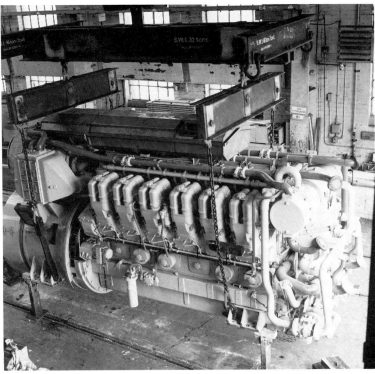

however, the speed of the traction motors also falls. With this reduction in speed comes a corresponding fall in the back emf, reducing the opposition to the motor current, which now rises automatically. More current equals more tractive effort, so the motors act like an automatic gearbox, effectively changing down a gear when 'hillclimbing'!

As the drawings have shown, the traction motors drive the wheels through spur reduction gears. These multiply the torque (turning effect) of the motor.

Power for the train

It is easy to forget that not all the power of the diesel engine reaches the driving wheels. A diesel locomotive needs power to drive the radiator fans, at least one main air compressor for the brakes, wipers, horns and for the heavy-duty, air-operated circuit breakers — the contactors — needed for switching and isolating purposes. To this list must be added current for the traction motor blower motors (these keep the traction motors cool), oil or coolant pumps, power for the battery-charging circuits (to start the diesel engine and for the lights), plus power for the train supply when air-conditioned or electrically-heated coaches are in tow.

The diesel engine is thereby robbed of as much as 450hp leaving a Class 47, for example, with a little over 2,200hp available for traction. An ac electric locomotive, in contrast, keeps its train supply and auxiliary supply away from the traction power circuitry, leaving all its rated power to move the train. Small wonder they can shift!

Finally, how do you start a 3,000hp diesel? A first-generation engine is started by applying current from the starting battery to the main generator which 'motors' until the engine starts. Modern, second-generation diesels with an alternator have two of the largest starter motors most people will ever see. These are designed to cope with the enormous starting currents needed to turn over a 12- or 16-cylinder engine. These are pretty reliable, which is just as well because they cost over £1,000 each!

The Refurbished Class 37s

A number of Class 37s have been overhauled and refurbished with many new items of traction and other equipment as part of a life extension programme.

The Class 37 is a mixed traffic (passenger and freight) diesel-electric locomotive, built by English Electric. A total of 308 units was produced, the first locomotive entering service on the Eastern Region in 1961. Powered by an

English Electric 12-cylinder turbocharged diesel engine of 1,750bhp, these 108-tonne Co-Co units feature a protruding nose end ahead of the driving compartment, giving them a transatlantic look.

The Class 37s are reliable workhorses, seen at their best working in pairs at the front of a heavy freight when the sound of 24 cylinders on full chat is an awe-inspiring

Below:
Unrefurbished Class 37 cutaway

Fig 27

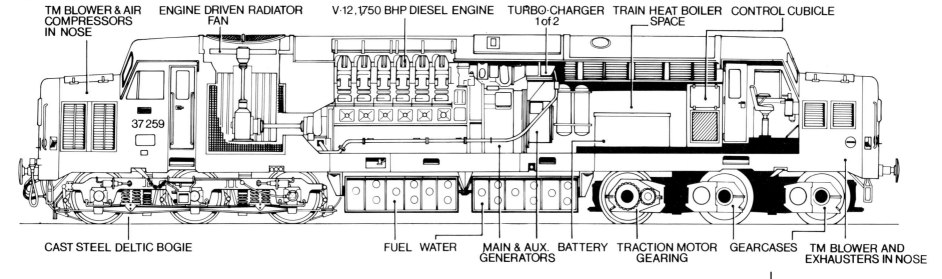

TM BLOWER & AIR COMPRESSORS IN NOSE

ENGINE DRIVEN RADIATOR FAN

V·12, 1,750 BHP DIESEL ENGINE

TURBO·CHARGER 1 of 2

TRAIN HEAT BOILER SPACE

CONTROL CUBICLE

37 259

CAST STEEL DELTIC BOGIE

FUEL   WATER

MAIN & AUX. GENERATORS

BATTERY

TRACTION MOTOR GEARING

GEARCASES

TM BLOWER AND EXHAUSTERS IN NOSE

experience. In recent years, however, their use on passenger services has been restricted. Most locomotives are for freight-only use, and the lack of an electric train supply (ETS) means they cannot be used on trains composed of air-conditioned stock except in dire emergencies!

New locomotives from old

BR's fleet of diesel locomotives was introduced into service over a relatively short period between the end of the 1950s and the beginning of the 1960s. Many will have reached the end of their working lives by the early 1990s and will need to be replaced by new locomotives within a relatively small timescale. To spread the introduction of new traction units over a longer period, it was decided to extend the life of selected locomotive classes including the Class 37 described here. Before the life extension programme could be authorised, however, the locomotives were subjected to the most searching examination by BR Board and Regional engineers to confirm that the proposed work was realistic,

would last for the extended life of the locomotives, and that any 'in service' problems would be eradicated at the same time.

Consultation with the Sector Directors showed there was a requirement for three principal types of Class 37 locomotive, a variety suitable for operating passenger trains and equipped with ETS, and two other types intended for freight working only. Of these, one would retain the existing axleload, and route availability of RA5, while the other would be ballasted to increase the adhesive weight to 120 tonnes to give increased haulage capability. This weight increase would give the heavier units a route availability of RA7.

The most important design change to the locomotive was the substitution of the troublesome main dc generator for a new Brush three-phase traction alternator, its ac output rectified (converted) to dc to power the traction motors. The motors, too, received attention, and with lower ratio gearwheels the locomotives now have greater tractive effort but with a reduction in maximum speed from 90 to 80mph.

Passenger locomotives have, in addition, a combined train supply and auxiliary (dual wound) alternator, the freight-only versions being provided with main and auxiliary alternators only. The train supply output is also three phase ac, fed to a train supply cubicle containing a separate rectifier to convert it to dc for the coaches. The locomotives have an ETS index of 30.

Using ac alternators in place of the heavier dc generators is a maintenance-saving ploy, introduced on the Class 56 heavy freight locomotive in 1976, the later Class 58, and Class 43 IC125 power cars. Modern alternators are brushless, using an inductive link to the diesel engine-driven rotor which in turn induces an alternating current to flow in the stationary stator windings surrounding the rotor. It is these stator windings which are connected via a main traction rectifier to the traction motors. A dc generator, by contrast, uses a large number of fixed carbon brushes to collect the traction current, each bearing against copper strips forming a drum-shaped commutator connected to the armature coils. The brushes and the commutator need regular and skilled maintenance to ensure efficient and reliable current collection, a task no longer necessary with alternator-equipped traction units.

Below:
Class 37 alternator

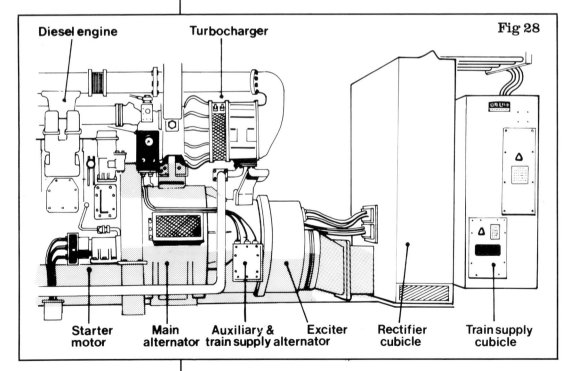

Fig 28

Diesel engine   Turbocharger

Starter motor   Main alternator   Auxiliary & train supply alternator   Exciter   Rectifier cubicle   Train supply cubicle

Electronics play a vital role in the rebuilt '37s'. The electromechanical load regulator and its associated resistances were largely replaced by an electronic equivalent which produces a small excitation current fed to an exciter mounted on the end of the alternators. This influences the magnetic field produced by the rotor and hence the current induced to flow in the stator, as previously mentioned. In this way, the exciter controls the much larger traction current passing to the traction motors.

This 'load regulation' function, carried out electronically, is necessary to balance the alternator output with its equivalent mechanical power from the diesel engine. Solid-state equipment with no moving parts is used, and is a further example of maintenance-saving design. All that remains of the old load regulator is the vane motor which was used to drive rotating contacts to introduce – or take

out – resistances in the main generator field windings to control its output.

On the refurbished locomotives this motor is now only coupled to a position transducer, a device that 'tells' the electronic load regulator how much power has been called for so the electronics can excite the main alternator rotor to produce a matching electrical output in the stator.

The electronics frame also contains a voltage regulator, traction motor field divert control unit, a temperature detector to monitor alternator and rectifier operating temperatures and, on freight-only versions, a slow-speed unit for operating merry-go-round (MGR) trains. It is not possible to 'motor' the main alternator for engine starting as is the case with conventional dc generator-equipped locomotives, and instead the '37s' are fitted with a pair of automobile-style starter motors fed from the battery. This last is protected by a low voltage detector in the starting circuitry.

The locomotives were completely rewired with new cables carried in trunking, the control cubicle receiving special attention. This was redesigned to accommodate the extra control equipment needed by the alternators and to take account of the Health & Safety at Work Act.

The exhauster isolating equipment was removed completely, the exhauster control switch being used for this purpose when required. A standard traction motor cut-out switch was also fitted.

There were no alterations to the trusty English Electric diesel engine apart from the fitting of heat shields in the 'V' between the two banks of six cylinders. Another modification was to the radiator fan which now has an electromagnetic clutch in the drive from the engine. The clutch is temperature controlled to ensure the fan runs only when required. This cost-saving equipment saves fuel, prevents overcooling of the engine and protects the radiators from damage in extreme weather conditions. The clutch is protected by a miniature circuit breaker and a switch is also provided for maintenance and test purposes. The cooling water header tank was replaced by a larger model.

A form of clean air compartment, HST style, was created by adding a bulkhead to the alternator end of the diesel engine. This improved the environment in and around the alternators, rectifiers and other electrical equipment. To this end, all the air entering the locomotive passes through dry, disposable filters.

Another internal modification was to the driving compartment which has improved sound insulation and better sealing against draughts. The cab doors, in particular, have improved sealing, and an added bonus for the driver is the fitting of cab seats to modern standards.

The locomotives' range was increased by converting the former boiler water tank into an additional fuel tank, a neat idea also used on some Class 47 locomotives. The emergency fuel tank, however, had to go, the space being needed for the larger radiator header tank. With increased fuel capacity, hopefully the emergency supply will not be missed!

Sharp-eyed readers will notice the louvres in the nose ends were increased in size as part of the measures taken to prevent draughts. This apparently illogical step, that of curing draughts by making the airflow easier, is a consequence of the traction motor blowers in the nose ends drawing air into their intakes through the cab. Sealing the cab bulkheads and making the louvres larger was a remedy the designers swear by.

The refurbished (life extension) locomotives fitted with ETS equipment are classified '37/4' and carry the numbers 37401 to 37431. Freight-only life extension locomotives are numbered from 37501 onwards for units with an RA5 route availability whilst the heavier, ballasted locomotives, with the more restrictive RA7 availability, are numbered upwards from No 37701.

Below:
Class 37 life extension: key features

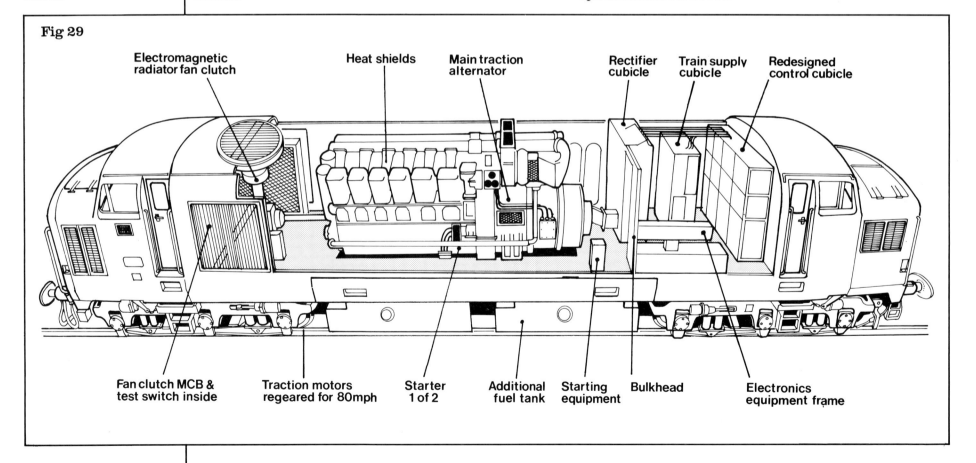

Fig 29

Electromagnetic radiator fan clutch — Heat shields — Main traction alternator — Rectifier cubicle — Train supply cubicle — Redesigned control cubicle

Fan clutch MCB & test switch inside — Traction motors regeared for 80mph — Starter 1 of 2 — Additional fuel tank — Starting equipment — Bulkhead — Electronics equipment frame

The Bournemouth Electrics

Introduction

The 24 Class 442 100mph EMUs are now in service on the Southern Region. All are BREL designed and built at Derby (Litchurch Lane) works. These sleek, highly attractive trains have brought current InterCity standards of comfort and amenity to the Waterloo-Southampton/Bournemouth and Weymouth route since it was dc electrified throughout in 1988. They will introduce for the first time Mk 3-style, 23m vehicles to Southern metals.

The trains also have a number of other features new to BR. They are BR's first five-car multiple-unit, the first with solid-state dc/ac static inverters for auxiliary supplies, the first with dot-matrix destination displays and the first main line trains to have power-operated swing/plug doors.

The Rolls-Royce of the Network — the Weymouth Electrics

Class 442 was designed to replace the 4-REP 'tractor' units introduced in 1967-74. For the benefit of readers unused to Southern Region EMUs, the 4-REPs were unique four-car units, able to propel two non-powered 4-TC units (with driving compartments and controls at each end) to Bournemouth, from where a single Class 33 diesel hauled the TC sets to Weymouth.

On the return journey, the units were propelled back to Bournemouth and recoupled to the 'REP' unit which then hauled the complete 12-car train back to Waterloo. This type of push-pull working was the first on BR; the link with the older trains remains, however, because much of their reliable power equipment — and their 400hp traction motors — was reconditioned and reused on the new trains.

The main drawing shows the complete train. Each five-car, 1,600hp unit is formed of a Driving Trailer Composite (DTC) with first class compartments and a small standard class saloon; a Trailer Standard (TS); a Motor Buffet Luggage Standard (MBLS) containing a conductor's 'office' between a pair of luggage compartments, a standard class saloon at one end and a buffet at the other (first class) end; a Trailer Open Standard Wheelchair (TSW) with space for a wheelchair; and a Driving Trailer Standard (DTS).

Two trains can run coupled together in a 10-car formation between London and Bournemouth. Lineside power supply constraints limit trains to a single five-car unit for the journey onwards to Weymouth, however.

The trains are fitted with a standard buckeye semi-automatic coupling at each end together with the normal air hoses and 27-way jumper cables. These were originally hidden away behind a lift-up cover — this can be seen on the close-up photograph of the front. The other sockets and

Fig 30

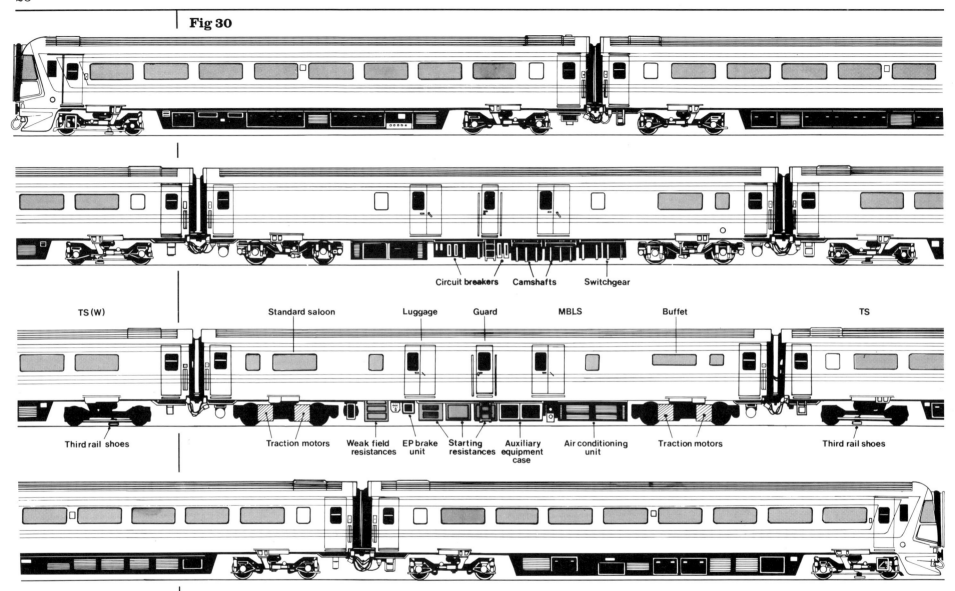

Circuit breakers   Camshafts   Switchgear

TS (W)   Standard saloon   Luggage   Guard   MBLS   Buffet   TS

Third rail shoes   Traction motors   Weak field resistances   EP brake unit   Starting resistances   Auxiliary equipment case   Air conditioning unit   Traction motors   Third rail shoes

Above:
Driving Trailer Composite (DTC)
Trailer Standard (TS)
Motor Buffet Luggage Standard (MBLS)
Trailer Standard Wheelchair (TSW)
Driving Trailer Standard (DTS)

hoses allow the train to be locomotive hauled over non-electrified routes.

Notice the dot-matrix destination display, operated by calculator-type push buttons inside the driving compartment. The driver simply enters a numerical code to make the display show the right destination. Another feature is the concertina-type exterior folding gangway doors which fold back when two trains are coupled together. Also noteworthy are the head, marker and tail lights cleverly mounted inside and below the curved windscreen.

Trailer cars are fitted with BT13 bogies similar to those on the Class 319 'Thameslink' trains while the BP20 power bogies (also from the Class 319 family) are host to the

4-REP's 400hp motors — a tight fit as some staff have seen for themselves!

The trains have air suspension and electropneumatically-operated disc brakes. Traction equipment is from withdrawn Class 432 (4-REP) units but with new starting resistances. Readers interested in traction may wonder why choppers, Class 319 style, were not used instead; the answer is that their main advantage is in the energy saved on trains with frequent stops. The Bournemouth trains, by contrast, spend much of their time on nonstop, comparatively long-distance runs, during which time the starting resistances are mostly switched out!

Construction of the vehicles was based on the Mk 3 coach but with a different floorpan. All the underframe-mounted equipment is designed for removal by forklift truck.

Exterior end doors are single leaf with a swing/plug action, and are operated by compressed air. Some of the doors may be isolated temporarily by the conductor's control panel at stations with short platforms.

Like their Mk 3 InterCity and HST counterparts, Class 442 trains have power-operated interior vestibule doors but with the difference that the door is without a pressure mat, instead opening when the handle is touched. A time delay switch closes it afterwards. Inside, the passenger saloons are air conditioned. One of the cars — the TSW — has a disabled persons' toilet and, adjacent to it, a space for a wheelchair. When not being used for this purpose, a pair of tip-up seats may be occupied by more fortunate passengers. A telephone booth is also provided.

The new generation

The Class 442 trains, flagships of Network SouthEast, are the most visible sign of a £37 million investment in trains and electrification equipment for use on Southern Region metals. The 24-strong fleet has brought a long-awaited new look to the South Western route to Southampton, Bournemouth and Weymouth. The trains swiftly became record breakers, performing a demonstration sprint to Weymouth in under 2hr when speeds of up to 109mph were reached.

The design of the five-car train is based on 23m Mk 3b locomotive-hauled trailer vehicles, using a single power car derived from a generator van produced by BREL for Irish Railways. A major design change to this vehicle was authorised to convert the luggage area nearest the buffet into a passenger lounge with seats and tables. This required the removal of two pairs of luggage doors and their replacement with windows.

Another modification was to convert all the standard class seating in the DTC vehicle to first class, making this coach a Driving Trailer First (DTF).

Left:
Close-up of the Class 442 front end. Notice the hatch covers below the windscreen housing the air hoses and jumper cables. Unfortunately these covers proved impractical in service and were later removed, giving a less satisfactory front end appearance.

Below:
Class 442 interior layout as originally built

Fig 31

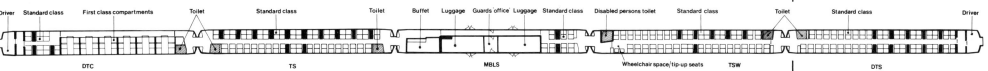

Reliable power

Recent ac overhead electric traction developments have
tended to overshadow the simple and reliable dc low-
voltage third rail system used on the Southern Region,
which boasts the most heavily used and extensive network
of this type in the world. Readers unused to Southern
Region electrics but familiar with their ac counterparts
may want to know how the Class 442 is controlled.

The simplified drawing on Fig 32 shows the basic
elements of a dc system. Power at 660V to 750V dc comes
from remotely controlled lineside substations where high
voltage ac from the CEGB is transformed and rectified
(changed) from ac to dc before being fed to the track via
cables. The insulated third rail forms one part of the circuit
to the train while one of the running rails forms the other.

Fig 33 shows how the current reaches the motors. Only
two have been shown to keep things simple. The
current-collecting shoes feed a continuous power train line

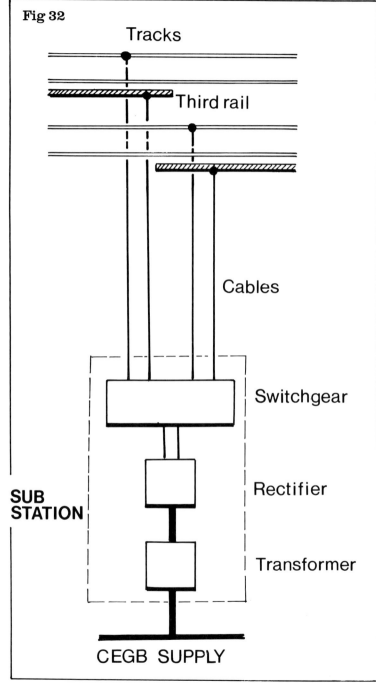

Fig 32

Tracks

Third rail

Cables

Switchgear

Rectifier

Transformer

SUB
STATION

CEGB SUPPLY

Fig 33

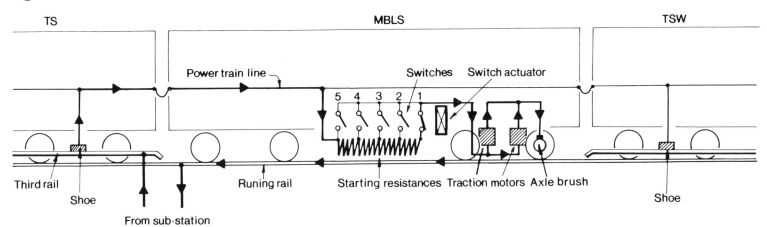

Left:
Traction current control
system.

which is in turn connected to the traction motors via starting resistances. These can be switched in or out automatically in response to the setting of the driver's four-notch power controller to vary the speed and tractive effort of the train. The resistances roughly approximate to the thyristors on ac multiple-unit trains and the dc choppers used on the dual-voltage Class 319 EMUs. All

basically produce a variable voltage for the motors from the fixed supply voltage. The path followed by the current at the lowest speed setting is arrowed, and the circuit back to the sub-station completed by axle brushes, the wheels and one of the running rails.

All the switches (numbered in Fig 33) above the resistances are made to open and close by a camshaft, like

Left:
**Standard class saloon
interior. The mainly blue
colour scheme echoes the
interior design of the
Class 319 'Thameslink'
EMUs.**

Below:
Interior of a typical first class
compartment. These are in a
smart red and grey colour
scheme with matt black
metalwork.

the one on diesel engines, and this is turned by an air/hydraulic camshaft actuator, hence the term 'camshaft control', familiar to Southern Region technical staff and drivers. It is fairly obvious that if the switches are closed individually and progressively in turn, the current will flow through a reduced amount of resistance and the train speed will gradually rise, or vice versa if the resistances are switched back in again. All this switching activity is responsible for the clicking sounds which can be heard coming from under the floor of a powered vehicle when the train is starting.

On the real train, however, the circuitry is a bit more complicated (and the train has more third rail shoes, to ensure it can negotiate gaps in the conductor rail at level crossings, for example) but the reader will get the general idea. Contrast all this electromechanical equipment with the semi-conductors and electronics in ac trains, whose control systems have no moving parts.

One innovation on the Class 442 is its electronically controlled, solid-state inverters used for auxiliary power. An inverter 'inverts' the dc from the third rail, artificially constructing a series of three forward and reverse ac cycles

Fig 34

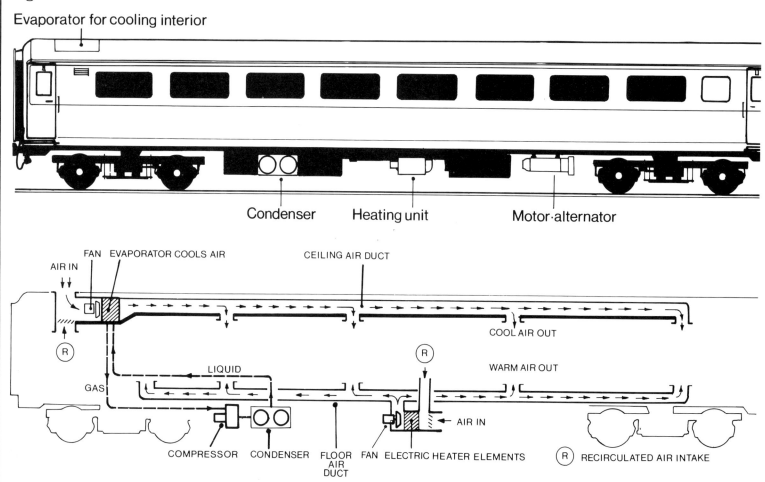

Evaporator for cooling interior

Condenser   Heating unit   Motor·alternator

Right:
Mk 2 d/e coach air-conditioning system

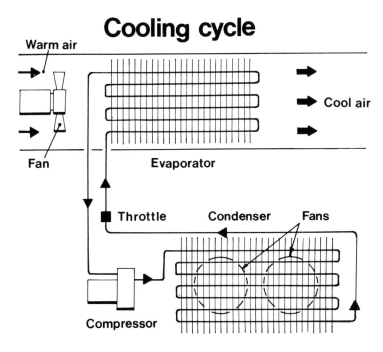

Fig 35

Cooling cycle

Warm air

Cool air

Fan

Evaporator

Throttle   Condenser   Fans

Compressor

to produce 415V ac three phase, mainly for the air-conditioning system plus lower voltage outputs for other equipment.

Cool it

The Wessex Electrics are the first Network SouthEast EMUs to be fitted with air conditioning and the first on BR to use a new 'heat pump' combined heating and cooling system.

To understand how this works, it is easiest to look first at conventional air conditioning. Fig 34 shows the air-conditioning system fitted to Mk 2d and 2e coaches in simplified form. The system has two parts, one to cool the coach and the other to heat it, the heating system similar to a fan heater blowing hot air through floor level ducts into the passenger saloon.

A preheating mode closes a set of shutters in the fresh air intake to recirculate the warm air. An evaporator situated

in a ceiling air duct cools the air blown over it by a circulating air fan, the air emerging from above head level. The evaporator is linked by piping to an underframe-mounted condenser which dissipates the heat absorbed in the system. Precooling also uses shutters, this time to recirculate cool air.

Fig 35 shows a cooling cycle like that in a domestic refrigerator. The coiled pipes in the evaporator are in the ice-making compartment and get very cold, while the condenser coils are the ones on the back of the refrigerator cabinet that get hot. Inside the pipes is a liquid that changes into a gas when heat is applied to it. Even a small amount of heat will be enough to do this, so when something at room temperature is put in the ice

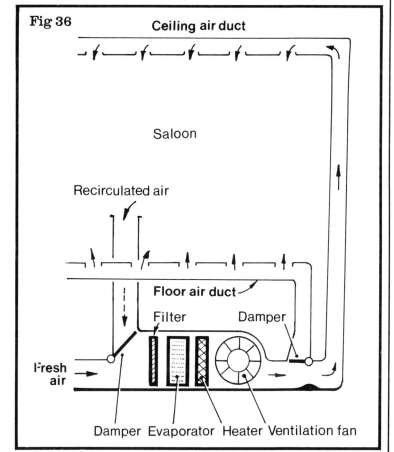

Fig 36

Ceiling air duct

Saloon

Recirculated air

Floor air duct

Filter   Damper

Fresh air

Damper Evaporator Heater Ventilation fan

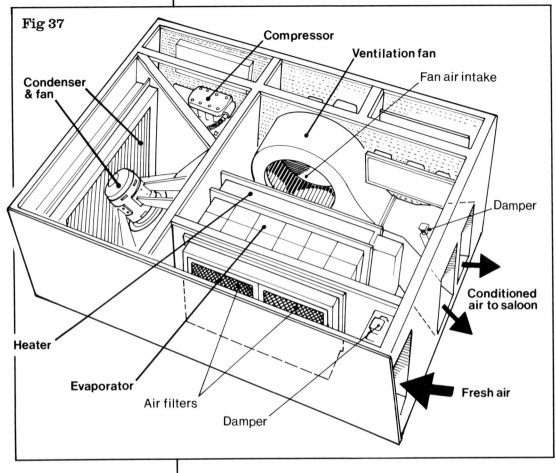

Fig 37

Compressor

Ventilation fan

Fan air intake

Condenser & fan

Damper

Conditioned air to saloon

Heater

Fresh air

Evaporator

Air filters

Damper

Above:
Air conditioning module.

the cooling cycle is repeated. A thermostat stops the compressor when the ice box is at the required low temperature.

Fig 36 shows part of an air-conditioning system for a Mk 3 coach while Fig 37 shows the air-conditioning module.

Enter the heat pump

The heat dissipated through the coils of a condenser is energy wasted, prompting engineers to design a 'reversible' refrigerator. This works like a refrigerator for cooling but can extract heat from the outside air (even though this air is at a relatively low temperature) and use it for heating. This is the principle of the 'heat pump' air-conditioning unit which uses clever electrical circuitry and changeover valves so that the evaporator can function as a condenser, and the condenser can act as an evaporator.

The system looks similar to that on a Mk 3 coach except that the coils in contact with the outside air are termed the outside coils and the pipes conditioning the coach interior are called, appropriately, the indoor coils. When the outside air temperature is very low, however, there is little heat to be extracted from the air by the outside coils so the heating deficiency is made up with electric heaters within the system.

The clever bit is that the six-cylinder compressor itself heats up the gas when it is compressed and some of this heat energy adds to the heat extracted from outside the coach. The compressor cylinders can effectively be isolated in pairs and this, plus a variable throttle, varies the heating or cooling to match the demand set by the thermostat. It also ensures that refrigerant is evaporated at a rate that will ensure no liquid reaches the compressor pistons! Energy savings of up to 40% are possible with the new system.

compartment, its heat is given up to the refrigerant (which becomes hotter) and the interior of the ice box gradually becomes colder.

The hot gas is then pumped by a compressor through a throttle to the condenser, the gas condenses back into a liquid (when it is cooled by air movement over the coils) and

Class 317/2 and 318 AC Electric Multiple-Units

Introduction

The first stage of the East Coast main line electrification from Hitchin to Peterborough required new multiple-unit trains to replace the existing DMU and diesel locomotive-hauled services. King's Cross outer suburban services were also re-equipped with the new trains and on ScotRail, the Ayrshire electrification scheme brought an expanded fleet of multiple-unit trains to provide services to the Ayrshire coast.

In the case of the GN line the new trains were 28 Class 317/2 four-car ac EMUs and Scotland saw what was essentially the same train — the three-car Class 318, numbering 20 units.

Body based on '125' coaches

Class 317 was planned for introduction in 1982 as the first in a new generation of 'standard' multiple-unit trains incorporating the highly successful construction techniques used for the 125mph Mk 3 coach.

To digress slightly, readers will recall that the previous 'standard' was the Class 313/314/315 ac units and the Class 507/508 dc trains. This design had driving motor cars at each end of a three or four-car set constructed of steel and aluminium. With a high proportion of motored axles, the trains were an obvious choice for dynamic (rheostatic) braking, a system which turns the traction motors into generators when braking. The current thus produced creates a retarding effect on the motor armatures, trying to slow them down; the traction motor gearing transfers this effect to the wheels.

Current is fed to resistance banks where it is dissipated as heat. In this way, the kinetic energy of the train is converted into heat, with maintenance-saving advantages on the air brake system, which is held off while current is flowing. As train speed reduces, the retarding effect is progressively diminished, the shortfall in braking being made up by blending in the air brakes automatically.

The Class 317 family reverts to the single power car design and, like all recent multiple-unit builds, has disc brakes, power-operated sliding doors, air suspension and public address equipment. All units are gangwayed throughout and may be coupled together with their fully automatic Tightlock couplers to form a maximum train length of 12 cars.

All Class 317/318 trains have four dc traction motors electronically controlled by solid-state thyristors which vary the voltage to the motors and, at the same time, convert the current from ac to dc. The original London Midland Region Class 317/1 units have toilet waste tanks to

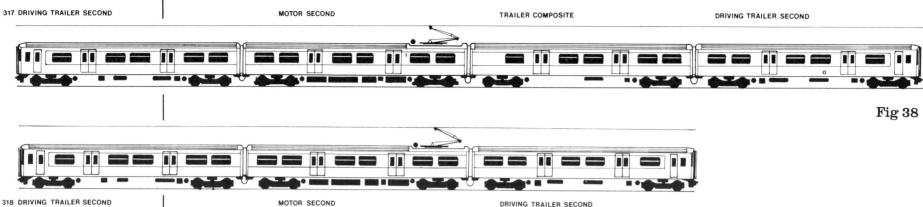

317 DRIVING TRAILER SECOND   MOTOR SECOND   TRAILER COMPOSITE   DRIVING TRAILER SECOND

Fig 38

318 DRIVING TRAILER SECOND   MOTOR SECOND   DRIVING TRAILER SECOND

Above:
Class 317 and 318 formations

allow them to work through the tunnels to Moorgate, a feature absent on the Class 317/2 variants.

Class 317 trains have a maximum speed of 100mph, allowing them to dash over the double-track GN sections, notably through the Welwyn Tunnels and over the adjacent viaduct, between 'flights' of HSTs. Both versions have first class accommodation, located in the middle of the trains.

A typical '317' unit is formed of a Driving Trailer Standard, Motor Standard, Trailer Composite and Driving Trailer Standard, and has seating for 295 passengers, including 22 in first class. The Class 318 is formed without the Trailer Composite vehicle. All '317s' have GEC electrical equipment; their Class 318 sister units have electrical equipment supplied by Brush Electrical Machines Ltd, and offer 227 standard class seats.

New suspension makes for a quieter, smoother ride

Air suspension is now the norm for all BR's new multiple-unit trains and locomotive-hauled coaches. Put at its simplest, air suspension consists of inflated air 'bags' — rather like the inner tubes of a lorry tyre, but with thicker walls — which are fixed in pairs on either side of the bogie frame, supporting the coach body. When combined with an efficient bogie of modern design, air suspension provides the passenger with a very smooth and quiet ride.

Air suspension has the advantage that it isolates the coach body from the bogies effectively, and it is this feature

which is mainly responsible for the lack of noise. Fig 39 shows how the system works, starting with the components (**1**).

The air bag is fed with compressed air at high pressure controlled by a levelling valve. In the position shown, imagine the air bag is pressurised and this keeps the coach body at a constant height above rail level. Now, if passengers get in and the load increases, the extra weight will compress the air bag and the coach body will sink to a lower level (**2**).

The fall in level will make the push rod (**1**) push the levelling valve open, air will enter the air bag, the internal air pressure will rise and start to lift the coach body to its former level. When this happens (**3**) the push rod will close the levelling valve, trapping the air inside, thereby maintaining the designed constant height above the rail.

Passengers leaving the train have the opposite effect, and the air pressure in the air bag will be too much, making the coach body rise. Air will be exhausted from the air bag until the coach body sinks to its correct level (**1**).

Such an air suspension system is therefore automatically self-levelling. A valuable spin-off from the air suspension system is load variable braking, something that is relatively easy to provide. Air bag pressure is dependent on, and proportional to, the passenger load; if this pressure is measured and sent to a variable load valve, this can interface with the brake system to adjust the braking rate automatically to suit the load.

Fig 39

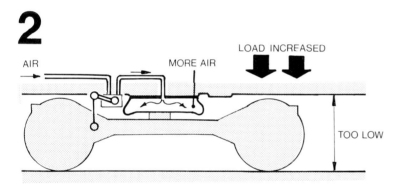

1

AIR SUPPLY

LEVELLING VALVE

AIR BAG

LOAD

HEIGHT

PUSH ROD

BOGIE

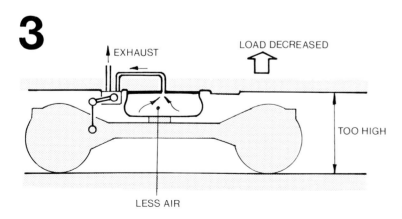

2

AIR

MORE AIR

LOAD INCREASED

TOO LOW

3

EXHAUST

LOAD DECREASED

TOO HIGH

LESS AIR

How the power is controlled

The ghosted underframe drawing of a Class 317/2 motor coach (Motor Standard) shown in Fig 40A is no different from the Class 317/1. A glance at the simple drawing of a multiple-unit basic power circuit (Fig 40B) shows that the train takes power from a feeder station (1) supplying the contact wire (2) at 25kV ac. Current is collected by the pantograph (3) linked to the main vacuum circuit breaker (4) connected by an internal cable to the transformer primary winding (5). This is in turn connected via another

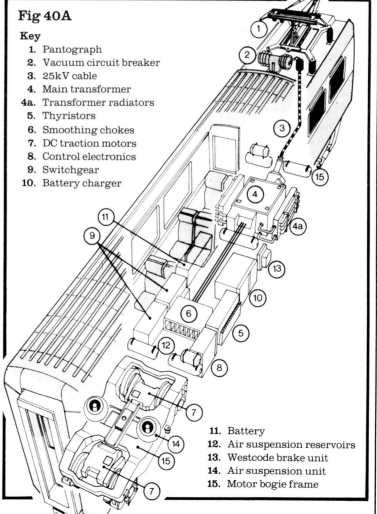

Fig 40A

Key

1. Pantograph
2. Vacuum circuit breaker
3. 25kV cable
4. Main transformer
4a. Transformer radiators
5. Thyristors
6. Smoothing chokes
7. DC traction motors
8. Control electronics
9. Switchgear
10. Battery charger

11. Battery
12. Air suspension reservoirs
13. Westcode brake unit
14. Air suspension unit
15. Motor bogie frame

Left:
Air suspension

Left:
Motor coach cut-away

Right:
Class 317/2 motor coach

Fig 40B

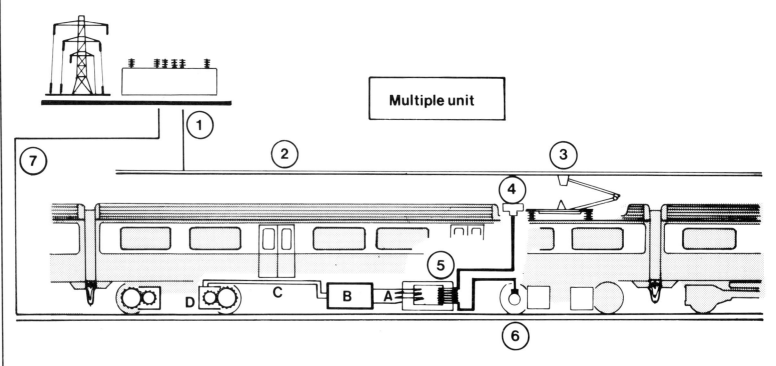

Multiple unit

cable to axle brushes, the current passing through the
wheels to one of the running rails (6), a trackside cable (7)
and back to the lineside feeder station (1). Such an
arrangement constitutes the basic electrical circuit between
the feeder station and the train.

The high voltage current flowing in the transformer
primary winding (5) induces a low voltage (1,000V) current
to flow in the transformer secondary winding (A) which is
fed to solid-state thyristors (B). These are basically fast
acting switches with no moving parts.

A single thyristor is slightly smaller than a 35mm film
canister and consists of layers of semiconductor materials
that will not allow a current to flow through until the
device is triggered (switched on) by a tiny electrical pulse.
When it does, a current will flow in one direction only.

If a thyristor is triggered at the same time in each
alternating current half cycle, a series of small pulses of
current will pass to the traction motor (D), one of four on
the motor coach. Smoothing chokes, not shown, are

connected in the circuit to the motors and act as a sort of
electrical flywheel, smoothing out the pulses so the motors
receive a steadier flow.

On the real train, a group of thyristors are combined with
rectifier diodes (devices like the thyristor but without the
switch) and can be made to pass longer or shorter pulses
according to the setting of the driver's power controller. If
full power is required, power is turned on continuously; if
low power is required and the driver selects a lower power
notch, the pulses will be very short. In this way, the power
to the motors can be varied infinitely so that the train can be
started from rest gently and then gradually worked up to
full power.

The main transformer also supplies power for other
electrical equipment. Current is needed for an air
compressor supplying air for the brakes, doors and air
suspension. The train also has to be heated and power is
needed for battery charging, lighting and for the train's
electronics and control systems.

Trains for 'Thameslink': Class 319 Dual-Voltage EMUs

Introduction

The main line tunnels from Farringdon to the Southern Region, now reopened, give Network SouthEast passengers from destinations on the Midland direct train services to Gatwick and Brighton. To work the service, new Class 319 trains were introduced, designed for dual-voltage operation on the 25kV ac overhead system and on the Southern's 750V dc third rail network. Like the Great Northern line Class 313 EMUs, the Class 319s are provided with both third rail shoes and roof-mounted pantographs, the changeover from one system to the other taking place at Farringdon.

The original order was for 46 units; although this was subsequently increased to 60 four-car trains, delivered from BREL's York works.

The '319s' were the first series production BR units to incorporate choppers. This section describes the choppers and how they work.

Pantographs and shoes

The '319s' are the second generation of dual-voltage EMUs to enter service on BR. The earlier Class 313 units were introduced in 1976 in three-car form with two power cars flanking a centre 'rectifier trailer', carrying a main transformer and rectifier, fed with ac from the overhead wires. The transformer reduced the voltage while the rectifier converted the ac into dc. Thus, the voltage from the transformer/rectifier matched the voltage from the third rail, a changeover switch connecting the dc motors to the selected system. The drawing shows how this was done. Note that the trains also have dynamic (electric rheostatic) braking; the circuitry for this has not been shown.

The resistance banks control the speed of the train, the driver's power controller and associated circuitry introducing (or taking out) resistances between the motors and the supply. It should be fairly obvious why the resistances are needed; the motors cannot accept full voltage from a standstill (they would very quickly burn themselves out), so power needs to be applied gradually and also very gently to prevent the wheels from losing their grip and spinning. Once the train gets underway, however, the resistances can be progressively and automatically switched out, until as speed increases the motors are able to accept full power.

The resistances, looking a bit like electric fire elements, simply heat up when they are in circuit and thus convert electrical energy into heat. Such a system is very widely used on BR, with the largest number of resistance controlled trains on the Southern Region, the resistances

Right:
Class 313 and 319 power
circuits

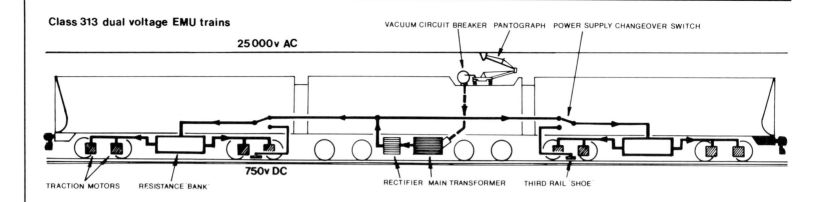

Class 313 dual voltage EMU trains

VACUUM CIRCUIT BREAKER PANTOGRAPH POWER SUPPLY CHANGEOVER SWITCH

25 000v AC

750v DC

TRACTION MOTORS   RESISTANCE BANK   RECTIFIER MAIN TRANSFORMER   THIRD RAIL SHOE

Fig 41

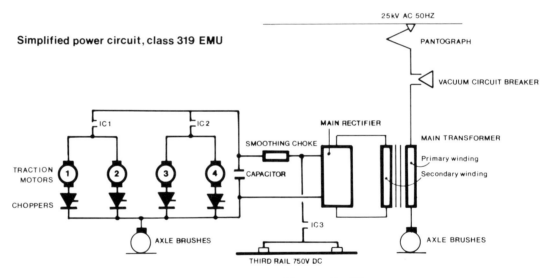

Simplified power circuit, class 319 EMU

25kV AC 50HZ

PANTOGRAPH

VACUUM CIRCUIT BREAKER

IC1   IC2   MAIN RECTIFIER   MAIN TRANSFORMER

SMOOTHING CHOKE   Primary winding

TRACTION MOTORS   CAPACITOR   Secondary winding

CHOPPERS

AXLE BRUSHES   IC3   AXLE BRUSHES

THIRD RAIL 750V DC

being switched by a camshaft turned by a rotary air/oil actuator.

Converting traction current into heat in this way, however, is a wasteful process and on trains with frequent stops there is a sizeable penalty in wasted energy. A reliable and more efficient alternative to this electromechanical system has now been developed, using solid-state devices called choppers. These are related to the silicon diodes found in rectifiers; how they control the motors of a train — and also save nearly 20% in energy costs — will be revealed in a moment.

On and off

A very much simplified drawing of a Class 319's power circuit shows that it is very similar in principle to that of the Class 313. The transformer and rectifier and the third rail both supply the same fixed voltage to the traction motors via choppers (on the left of the drawing) rather than by the resistance banks of the '313'. The motors can be isolated in pairs by the isolating switches (IC1 and IC2); IC3 selects dc third rail once the pantograph has been lowered.

Fig 42 shows the principle of a chopper. Here, an electric motor, corresponding to one on the Class 319, is connected to a supply via a switch. It would be possible to control the speed of the motor by the switch alone if it could be turned on and off very rapidly, several hundred times a second. This is basically what a chopper does. For it to work, however, some kind of timing device is needed accurately to divide time into precise intervals. This is provided by electronic circuitry under the control of a computer. Turning the switch on for only a tiny part of each time interval is equivalent to the motor operating on a low voltage and with limited power.

This can be seen in more detail in Fig 43, showing how long the switch — the chopper — is turned on in each of these time intervals, known as the 'chopping period'. The horizontal scale represents time. The 'on' periods are called 'mark' and the 'off' periods are known as 'space'. Then, in Fig 44, the amount of time the chopper is switched on has been increased so that now it spends half its time turned on and the other half turned off, equivalent to the motor operating on half voltage.

So, the mark/space ratio — the proportion of 'on' time to 'off' time — determines the voltage, which can therefore be controlled in an infinitely variable way. Turning the chopper on continuously will leave the supply unaltered and the motor will operate on full line voltage. The characteristic shape of the drawings makes them appear like a log of wood chopped into slices, hence the term 'chopping' being used to describe what is happening to the circuit.

Put another way, the chopper works by 'chopping up' the fixed supply voltage to reduce the mean dc voltage applied to the motors.

A chopper, as we have seen, is a solid-state device with no moving parts and is therefore virtually maintenance-free. Its other main advantage, however, is the all-important energy-saving one, since little or no energy is converted wastefully into heat. As mentioned earlier, the choppers and power control circuitry on the Class 319 are computer controlled, like the Class 89, 90 and 91 electric locomotives, the driver's power controller signalling to it his demand for power or otherwise. Four power notches are provided. Notch 1 is used for shunting, Notch 2 allows the unit to accelerate appropriately up to half power while Notch 3 produces full power. The last notch produces maximum

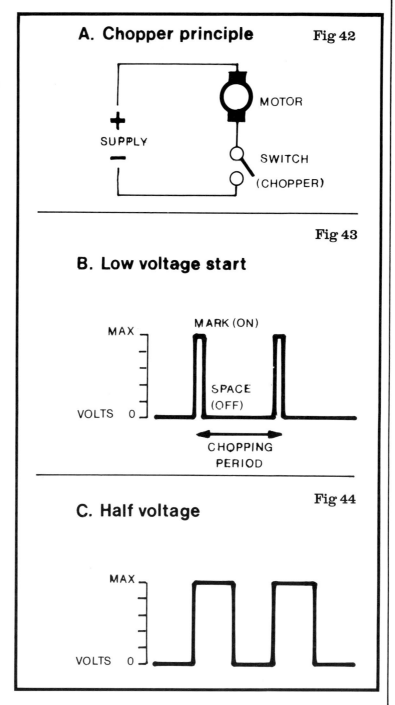

A. Chopper principle Fig 42

MOTOR

SUPPLY

SWITCH

(CHOPPER)

Fig 43

B. Low voltage start

MARK (ON)

MAX

SPACE
(OFF)

VOLTS 0

CHOPPING
PERIOD

Fig 44

C. Half voltage

MAX

VOLTS 0

speed, and to achieve it the motors are put automatically into what is called 'weak field'. This simply means the stationary field windings of the motors have a resistance deliberately introduced to weaken them, thereby lessening the natural tendency of the motors to act as generators. Thus, the applied voltage can rise and the motors will increase speed to maximum.

The trains

The BREL-built Class 319 EMUs are based on the earlier Class 317 design but with some detail differences. They have gangways, but not between sets when working in multiple. One other difference is the very distinctive and attractive front end with a hinged centre door for emergency exit. Inside, the new trains have high backed seating, as befits their longer distance role, and the end walls feature a series of murals showing landmarks. Like all recent EMU builds, the trains have power-operated sliding doors, air suspension and air-operated disc brakes. Driving compartments at each end are entered through dedicated sliding doors which are also power operated. GEC supplied all the power equipment for these units.

Fig 45 shows the equipment under the two centre cars. The train is composed of a pair of Driving Trailer Standard (DTS) vehicles, a Pantograph Motor Standard (PMS) and an Auxiliary Trailer Standard (ATS).

Right:
Class 319 roof-mounted pantograph.

Far right:
Class 319 driver's sliding door.

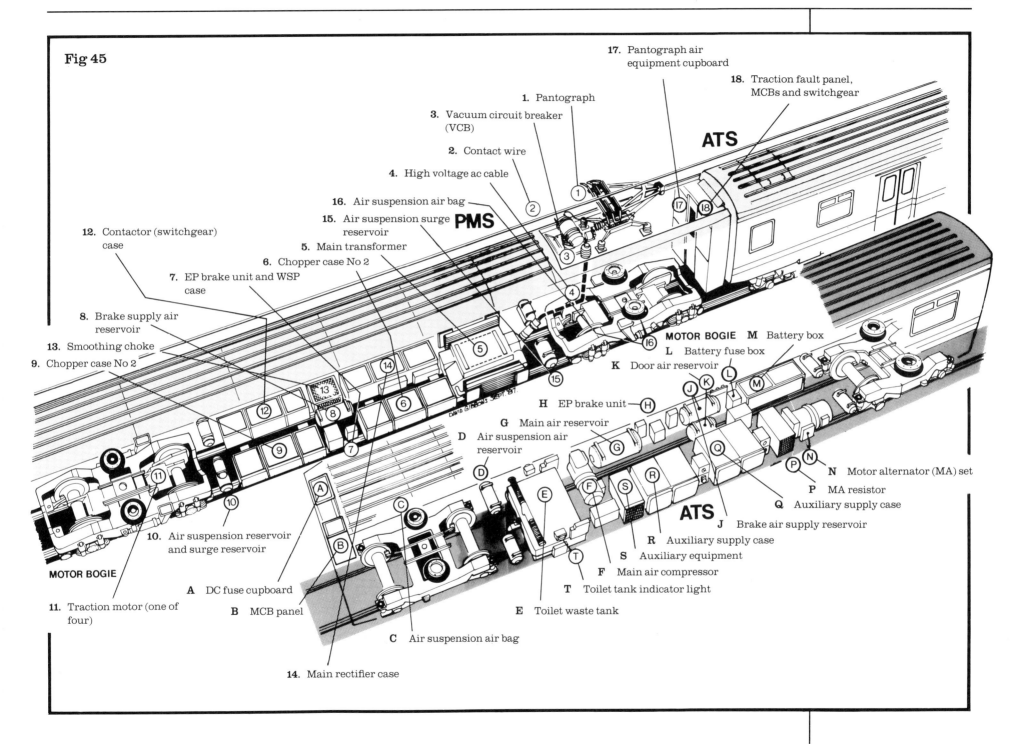

Fig 45

17. Pantograph air equipment cupboard

18. Traction fault panel, MCBs and switchgear

1. Pantograph

3. Vacuum circuit breaker (VCB)

2. Contact wire

4. High voltage ac cable

16. Air suspension air bag

15. Air suspension surge reservoir

5. Main transformer

6. Chopper case No 2

7. EP brake unit and WSP case

12. Contactor (switchgear) case

8. Brake supply air reservoir

13. Smoothing choke

9. Chopper case No 2

10. Air suspension reservoir and surge reservoir

11. Traction motor (one of four)

A. DC fuse cupboard

B. MCB panel

C. Air suspension air bag

14. Main rectifier case

D. Air suspension air reservoir

E. Toilet waste tank

F. Main air compressor

T. Toilet tank indicator light

S. Auxiliary equipment

R. Auxiliary supply case

G. Main air reservoir

H. EP brake unit

J. Brake air supply reservoir

Q. Auxiliary supply case

P. MA resistor

N. Motor alternator (MA) set

M. Battery box

L. Battery fuse box

K. Door air reservoir

MOTOR BOGIE

ATS

PMS

ATS

MOTOR BOGIE

DAVID GIBBONS SEPT 87

The Anglia Electrics: Class 321 Trains for Euston to Northampton, Cambridge and Southend Services

Sleek at the front

Anglia Region was the destination of the first batch of BREL-built Class 321 four-car ac EMUs. These are gradually replacing 30-year-old slam-door stock of Classes 302 and 305/2 used on Cambridge and Southend services. Class 321 trains have also entered service on Euston line outer-suburban services to Birmingham via Northampton.

A total of 46 units was originally ordered (the first being delivered six weeks ahead of schedule), and to this was added a follow-on order for 30 more trains, together with another 20 Class 319 units. All are York-built, the Class 321s being intended for 25kV ac operation and maintained at Anglia's Ilford depot. They are based on the Class 319 BREL/GEC 'Thameslink' dual-voltage trains, but with Brush electrical equipment similar to that on the Class 318 units built for the Ayr electrification. Unlike the '317s', whose bodyshell they share, there is no front end gangway connection or emergency door, the driver looking ahead through a pair of sloping windows above a lifting panel designed to give maintenance access to internal equipment. Below this is a valance, Class 442 style, that completes a radically different front end design.

Taking a leaf from the Class 319's book, the '321s' also have murals on the end panels in the saloons. These depict typical rural scenes from areas served by the units, rendered in colourful style. First class accommodation is at one end, located in one of the driving trailer vehicles behind the driving compartment. The designers had second thoughts about the first class saloons and the layout was changed in the London Midland Region builds with the new design being gradually applied retrospectively to the earlier Anglia units. Also carried over from the Class 319 is direct entry into the driving compartments using power-operated plug-type side doors, thereby abolishing the cross vestibule used on earlier Class 317-based units.

A complete four-car unit is composed of a Driving Trailer Composite (DTC) with first and standard class seating, and a Pantograph Motor Standard (PMS). This vehicle has standard class accommodation only and incorporates all the power equipment including the pantograph and underslung main transformer, with four Brush traction motors driving the axles of the two motor bogies. The main drawing shows how the equipment is located on the underframe. Next to this is marshalled an Auxiliary Trailer Standard (ATS), also with standard class seats only, and two toilets at the PMS end. The single main air compressor, reservoir and compressor controls and an auxiliary supply equipment case is mounted under this vehicle. The

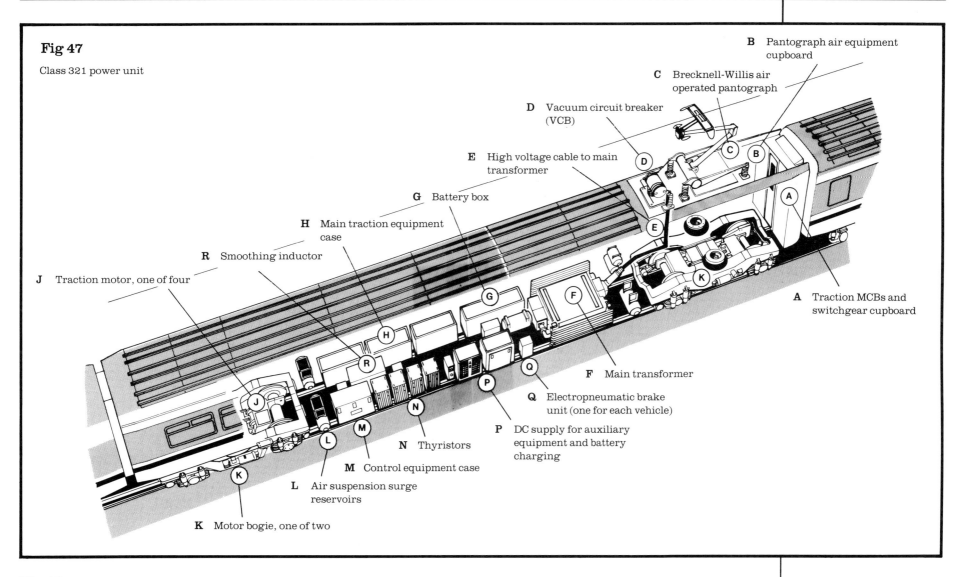

Fig 47

Class 321 power unit

B Pantograph air equipment cupboard

C Brecknell-Willis air operated pantograph

D Vacuum circuit breaker (VCB)

E High voltage cable to main transformer

G Battery box

H Main traction equipment case

R Smoothing inductor

J Traction motor, one of four

A Traction MCBs and switchgear cupboard

F Main transformer

Q Electropneumatic brake unit (one for each vehicle)

P DC supply for auxiliary equipment and battery charging

N Thyristors

M Control equipment case

L Air suspension surge reservoirs

K Motor bogie, one of two

Fig 46   Class 321 formation

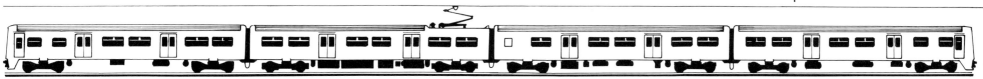

DRIVING TRAILER COMPOSITE   PANTOGRAPH MOTOR STANDARD   AUXILIARY TRAILER STANDARD   DRIVING TRAILER STANDARD

formation is completed with a Driving Trailer Standard (DTS). This has a lockable convertible passenger/parcels area and a standard class saloon. To assist platform staff in identifying it, this vehicle carries a 'P' suffix to its operating number, painted on the front.

Like all recent multiple-unit builds, the Class 321s have air suspension, Westcode-compatible air-operated disc brakes by Davies & Metcalfe (with load variable braking determined by air suspension pressure) and powered sliding doors. The outer ends are fitted with Tightlock automatic couplers (requiring no side buffers), which are controlled by push buttons in the driving compartments. Up to 12 cars can be coupled together, the automatic coupler joining all the necessary electrical and pneumatic connections. Coaches are semi-permanently coupled within a set with bolted bar couplings similar to those linking Freightliner wagons. Corridor connections are also provided between the vehicles.

The driver has a comfortable driving compartment with excellent visibility. Controls and instruments are identical to the Class 319 but minus the push buttons and indicators needed for dual-voltage operation.

Controlling the power

The power control system is electronically controlled using solid-state thyristors to control the four Brush dc traction motors. Thyristor-based control systems are now standard equipment on most second-generation ac EMUs, and on the Class 89, 90 and 91 locomotives.

Thyristors take the place of the complex electro-mechanical high voltage transformer tap changers used on some early EMUs, and on Class 86 and 87/0 locomotives, to produce a variable voltage for the motors.

As technically-minded readers will know, the thyristor is a solid-state device related to silicon rectifier diodes and with no moving parts. Put at its simplest, a thyristor is a fast acting switch, which operates like a controlled rectifier and converts the ac from the main transformer into variable voltage dc. Readers will find at least one inside their lighting dimmer switches; those in the power control system of an EMU or locomotive work in the same way, with the same effect of the motors as the dimmer switch has on the lights, but on a larger scale.

Right:
The neatly styled front end of the Class 321 'Anglia Electrics'.

How the thyristor operates is described in the chapter on the Class 317-8 EMU trains . Although the voltage applied to the motors is infinitely variable, the driver nevertheless has four power notches, each one setting an upper limit for power; thus, Notch 1 is used for coupling or other low speed operations, Notch 2 will gradually produce half power, while Notch 3 will allow the train to accelerate progressively until full power is applied. Notch 4 is reserved for full speed and in this position the traction motor field windings have resistances automatically inserted in circuit with them to reduce their natural tendency to act as generators, thereby opposing the applied voltage and limited speed. Field weakening allows the applied voltage to be increased, making the motors accelerate still further to a maximum service speed of 100mph when required.

The next generation

The re-equipment of Network SouthEast with new trains will take a major step forward in 1990 when the first of the 'Networker' trains is introduced into service. This all-new design will mark the end of the Mk 3 coach-based Class 317 family of units, both ac and dc versions of which have appeared north and south of the Thames. This basic bodyshell with front variations has been used for Class 319, the Class 321 illustrated here, the Southern Region Class 455/456 and for the forthcoming Class 322 units for Stansted Airport services. Scotland is also a user of the design, both with its Class 318 trains for Ayrshire and the similar Class 320. Both these types were introduced in three-car form.

Prior to this was the Class 313 family, a 1970s design first used on the Great Northern dual-voltage Class 313 trains. From these came similar dc-only units of Class 507 for the London Midland Region and Class 508 for the Southern. The Southern units were later transferred to the London Midland (minus a trailer coach for use in some batches of Class 455 trains) for operation on the Merseyrail system.

In Network SouthEast service the various classes have now received route branding, carrying such names as 'Northampton Line' and 'Anglia Electrics'. The list below shows some of the current titles.

'Great Northern' (red)	Class 313 King's Cross inner suburban
'North London Lines'	Class 313 Euston-Watford
'Great Northern' (blue)	Class 317 King's Cross outer suburban
'Northampton Line'	Class 317/321 Euston-Northampton
'Thameslink'	Class 319 Bedford-Brighton
'Anglia Electrics'	Class 321 Liverpool Street suburban
'South Western Lines'	Class 455/456 South Western suburban
'South London Lines'	Class 455 South Central suburban
'Stansted Express'	Class 322 Liverpool Street-Stansted

The high-tech 'Networker' will start a new EMU family, and will feature a rounded, semi-streamlined front end (pictured above) with no gangways. High-backed seats, on-train electronic information displays showing destination and calling points (and fare bargains!) and improved heating and ventilation will be part of an interior package bearing little or no resemblance to its predecessors. The trains will appear in Class 465 dc inner-suburban and Class 471 outer-suburban form for service on Southern Region routes, while its ac counterpart will be the Class 331 for the London, Tilbury & Southend route. It is also destined for non-electrified routes in diesel-powered Class 165 'Chiltern Turbo' and 'Thames Turbo' form, intended for Paddington and Marylebone suburban duties.

Electric Networkers will also feature ac brushless, low-maintenance traction motors, now under test fitted to the former Class 210 prototype DEMU, reclassified as Class 316. These motors employ solid-state inverters, similar in principle to those used for auxiliary power on the Class 442 'Wessex Express' units, and able to produce a variable voltage and frequency three phase output from a single phase source.

Enter the Class 89

Introduction

The prototype Class 89 ac electric locomotive was a notable first on BR for several reasons. It was BR's first six-axle (Co-Co) ac electric locomotive and was the first high speed ac traction unit with a 125mph capability (other than APT) to operate on BR tracks. It was also the first ac locomotive to enter service since 1975 when the Class 87/1 prototype was introduced as a follow-on from the Class 87/0 order for the WCML electrification to Glasgow.

BREL's Crewe works was responsible for the mechanical parts and final assembly of the Brush-designed and equipped 5,800hp locomotive. As the chapter on 'InterCity 225' explains, the locomotive was originally intended as the power unit for the ECML electrification to Leeds, Newcastle and Edinburgh but is now regarded as a possible fall-back option if the Class 91 'Electra' locomotive fails to live up to expectations. This elegant, streamlined locomotive is a powerhouse indeed and is greatly admired by all the drivers trained to operate it.

The Class 89 weighs in at 105 tonnes, is 64.9ft long and has a maximum speed of 125mph. It can operate at line voltages down to 16.25kV and is fitted with a Brecknell-Willis current-collecting high speed pantograph connected through a VCB on the roof to a main transformer mounted under the integrally constructed superstructure between the bogies. The transformer is flanked by a pair of batteries. One of these is for the controls and lighting while the other produces a dedicated supply for the dynamic brake.

Inside, the locomotive has a central corridor running from end to end between the two cabs, with the main items of electrical equipment, including the motor-driven twin air compressors, arranged on either side of it. Brush has used a number of glass-reinforced plastic (GRP) panels on the locomotive, particularly in the air-conditioned driving compartments, to good effect. Externally, similar GRP mouldings give the '89' a smooth, streamlined and highly attractive appearance; it is particularly photogenic and looks good from most angles.

The driving compartments themselves are very similar to those of the Class 43 IC125 power car, echoing its control layout and E70 electrically-operated automatic air brakes. The Class 89 is also fitted with dynamic (rheostatic) electric braking, but more of this later. Like the Class 90 and 91 locomotives, the Brush unit has microprocessor (computer)-controlled twin thyristor 'power packs' powering its six SEPEX dc traction motors. This system gives notchless control of tractive effort.

The '89' is also fitted with a speed selector which sets maximum speed in 5mph increments up to 125mph, while the driver's power controller basically sets the rate of

'A' SIDE INTERIOR EQUIPMENT

Fig 48

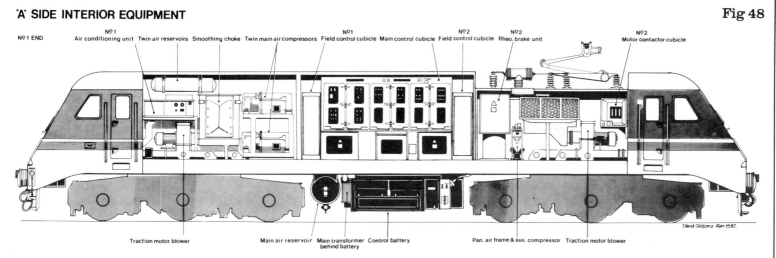

'B' SIDE INTERIOR EQUIPMENT

Fig 49

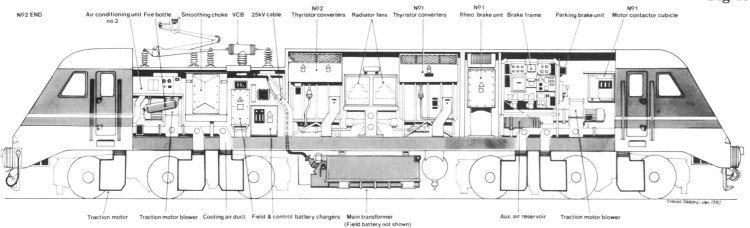

acceleration. Thus when starting from rest with no temporary or permanent speed restrictions, if the power controller is opened fully with the line speed set at, say, 125mph, the locomotive will accelerate very rapidly to its maximum speed.

Sensors in the traction motor circuits ensure that motor current limits are not exceeded. How much power is available will be worked out by the computer, taking account of the load, the condition of the rails, the line

voltage, the speed selected and the rate of acceleration, set, as before, by the driver's power controller. Such a system is the rail traction equivalent of the 'cruise control' fitted to some up-market cars. Once set, it will maintain a constant speed, although it should be emphasised the driver will continue to have overall control of his locomotive.

Like the Class 90 and 91 locomotives, the '89' is now equipped for push-pull working from a remote driving trailer using a TDM system. This sends appropriate control signals along the RCH lighting cables within the train, its principle of operation being the separation of time into accurate 'time divisions'. Thus, at one time interval, a traction control signal will be sent down the cable and, at the next, speech (or the guard's signal buzzer) and so on. Such time intervals last for only fractions of a second, the timing accuracy needed to send the signals at the right time being well within the capability of modern electronics. This feature is discussed in the next chapter.

Slipping wheels

Wheelslip occurs when the driving wheels lose their grip and spin, like a car's wheels on an icy road. This can be caused by wet or greasy rails, the lack of adhesion (grip) causing train-handling problems for the driver on high-powered electric locomotives. The notchless control provided by the thyristor can, with microprocessor control tailor precisely the tractive effort to match the available

Right:
Class 89 internal layout

Below:
This photograph clearly illustrates the striking styling of the Brush Class 89. The locomotive has since been painted in the latest InterCity livery style.

Fig 50

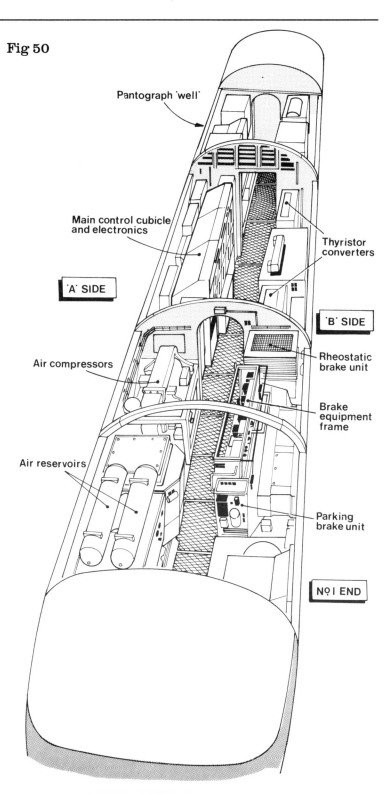

Pantograph 'well'

Main control cubicle and electronics

'A' SIDE

'B' SIDE

Thyristor converters

Air compressors

Rheostatic brake unit

Brake equipment frame

Air reservoirs

Parking brake unit

Nº1 END

adhesion, something almost impossible to achieve with a tap changer.

The Class 89 is fitted with an EW2 wheelslip/slide system by Davies & Metcalfe. This employs a total of six miniature alternators, one on each axle. A slipping wheel is detected by comparing the six output voltages; tractive effort in the offending axle is then reduced appropriately. If, however, all the wheels slip simultaneously, this is detected by measuring the rate of acceleration of each axle. Correction is by reducing power. The EW2 system incorporates a self-diagnostic and test facility.

Dynamic braking

The Class 89 is fitted with dynamic (rheostatic) electric braking that is independent of the line voltage. It is the primary braking system, the traction motor field windings being energised (in braking) from a separate 'field' battery supply to make it proof against overhead line power supply breakdowns. It works on the principle that converting the traction motors into generators during braking will provide a retarding effect on the motor armatures and, hence, through the motor gearing to the wheels.

The current produced is dissipated through a pair of rheostatic brake units containing resistances that glow red hot, thus converting the kinetic energy of the train into heat. This is dissipated to atmosphere by fans. As speed falls, however, current output falls and with it the retarding effect, so at around 31mph the automatic airbrake is blended in automatically finally to bring the train to a stand.

If a fault occurs, train speed is automatically reduced to bring the braking duty within the capacity of the air (tread) brake. The EW2 system also controls the dynamic brake so that wheelslide is corrected by reducing the braking effort, either air or dynamic, until the wheels start to rotate once again.

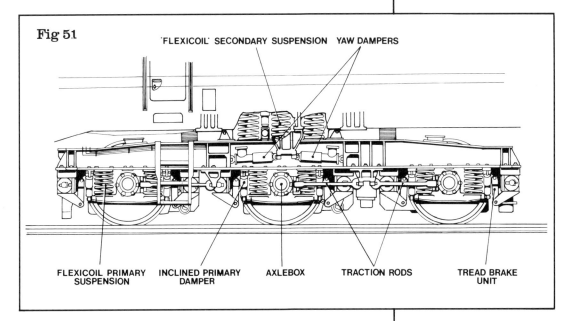

Fig 51

'FLEXICOIL' SECONDARY SUSPENSION   YAW DAMPERS

FLEXICOIL PRIMARY SUSPENSION   INCLINED PRIMARY DAMPER   AXLEBOX   TRACTION RODS   TREAD BRAKE UNIT

Above:
Class 89 bogie

Bogies

The bogies on the Class 89 are to a new design (see Fig 51). Space does not allow for a full description of the bogie, but suffice to say Brush claims that its design performs acceptably on curves at high speed. Unlike conventional three-axle bogies, all axles (not just the centre one) can 'float' laterally in a controlled way, so that the lateral sideways loads on the track when curving at speed are minimised. Thus, the primary suspension coil springs and inclined telescopic dampers control lateral movements while traction and braking forces are imparted to the bogie frame by longitudinal traction rods. Secondary suspension to support the body is also by coil springs mounted in 'nests' above the bogie frame. The design was produced using the resources of BR's Research & Development Division.

New Power for the West Coast Main Line

Introduction

The Class 90 is the first new series-production ac electric locomotive to appear since the Class 87s heralded electric working from London to Glasgow in 1973. Designed for passenger and freight working, the Class 90 design is bringing a new look to West Coast operation with its matching Driving Van Trailers for push-pull working.

The Class 90 ac electric locomotive

The Class 90 is a 4,850hp locomotive, designed and built by BREL at Crewe with GEC electrical equipment. An initial build of 29 110mph locomotives for the West Coast main line and North London Line is being followed by a further 21 units to operate freight services and some passenger trains on the East Coast main line, now being electrified.

The Class 90 design is ahead of the Class 91 IC225 high speed locomotives for the ECML electrification, and has similar power equipment including its microprocessor (computer)-based traction control system. This provides automatic fault logging for maintenance purposes and speed preselection by the driver, a system first seen on the Class 89 prototype ac electric locomotive.

The Class 90 – originally to have been classified '87/2' – is a compact, four-axle, 85-tonne Bo-Bo locomotive, 18,800mm (61.6ft) long with an interior equipment layout between the driving compartments closely following the existing Class 86 and 87 designs, as Fig 52 shows.

Four 'power packs' are located at the corners, each containing a traction motor blower and smoothing choke, the rectifier modules of the earlier classes being replaced with air-cooled thyristor 'converters'. The operation of the thyristor is described elsewhere. They produce a variable voltage for the traction motors with notchless control of tractive effort, and form the electronic equivalent of the electromechanical tap changer fitted to first-generation ac traction.

Like the existing Class 87s on which the '90s' are based, the main transformer occupies the centre portion of the locomotive, and is flanked by a pair of rheostatic (dynamic) brake units each containing braking resistors and cooling fans. At the No 2 end is a neat brake equipment frame and next to it, on the third power pack, is the main switchgear panel containing miniature circuit breakers (MCBs), both easily accessible by the driver if a fault requires equipment to be isolated. Drivers used to Class 86 and 87 locomotives will immediately feel at home on the new locomotives.

Air-conditioned driving compartments are provided at each end to a new design that is broadly similar to the Class 89 and 91 locomotives. A photograph shows the layout; the driver's seat is as comfortable as it looks. All the braking controls are on the left while the power controls are on the right. Notice the tiny power controller, little bigger than a conventional horn control. This basically selects the rate of acceleration to a speed set by the speed controller, on the left of, and adjacent to the speedometer.

Externally, the locomotive embodies the new 'house style' set by the Class 91, but with a less steeply raked front end, and the new bodyshell is a considerable visual improvement on the highly functional Class 87/0 and 87/1 design. The front end (which, incidentally, carries a buckeye coupler) is reinforced to give improved collision protection to UIC standards.

The bogie is the BP9 fitted to the Class 87s, the frame-mounted traction motors having similar flexible drives to the axles. A major success story of the Class 87 fleet has been the traction motors themselves which have proved to be among the most reliable on BR; a separately excited version is fitted to the new locomotives.

Four of the class are for use on cross-London freight and other services over the newly-electrified North London line.

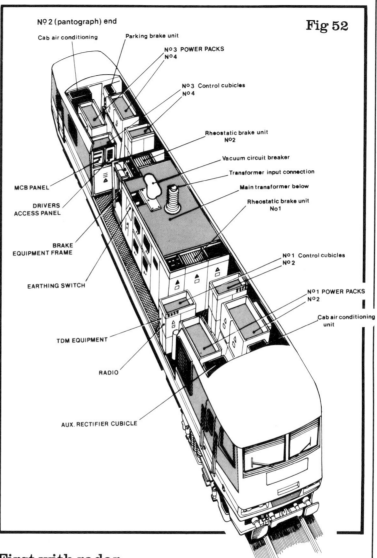

Fig 52

Nº 2 (pantograph) end
Cab air conditioning
Parking brake unit
Nº 3 POWER PACKS
Nº 4
Nº 3 Control cubicles
Nº 4
Rheostatic brake unit Nº2
Vacuum circuit breaker
Transformer input connection
Main transformer below
Rheostatic brake unit No1
MCB PANEL
DRIVERS ACCESS PANEL
BRAKE EQUIPMENT FRAME
Nº 1 Control cubicles
Nº 2
EARTHING SWITCH
Nº 1 POWER PACKS
Nº 2
Cab air conditioning unit
TDM EQUIPMENT
RADIO
AUX. RECTIFIER CUBICLE

First with radar

Wheel creep control – the control of wheel slip – is a feature of the Class 90, using the same principle as the Foster Yeoman General Motors Class 59. It is also fitted to the Class 91s.

The accurate control of wheel creep needs a parallel system of precise speed measurement, and on the Class 90 a Doppler radar, like that on the Class 59s, gives an

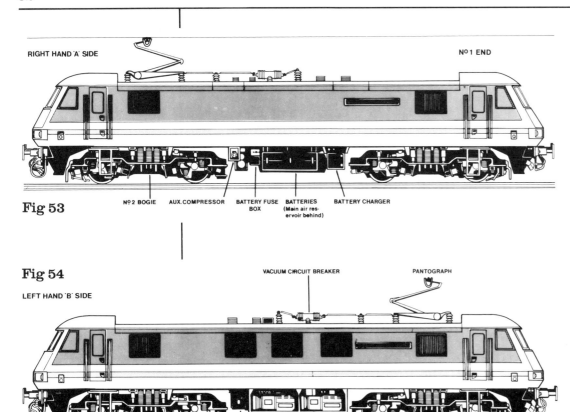

RIGHT HAND 'A' SIDE   N⁰ 1 END

Fig 53

N⁰ 2 BOGIE   AUX. COMPRESSOR   BATTERY FUSE BOX   BATTERIES (Main air reservoir behind)   BATTERY CHARGER

Fig 54

LEFT HAND 'B' SIDE

VACUUM CIRCUIT BREAKER   PANTOGRAPH

N⁰ 1 END   N⁰ 1 BOGIE   SURGE SUPPRESSION EQUIPMENT   MAIN AIR COMPRESSORS

Top:
Class 90 'A' side exterior equipment

Above:
Class 90 'B' side exterior equipment

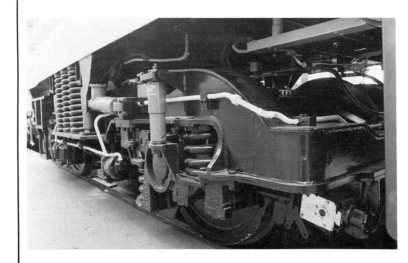

Right:
Class 90 bogie, showing Flexicoil suspension.

independent and extremely accurate indication of groundspeed that does not depend on wheel rotation (a conventional locomotive uses an axle-driven generator to produce a speed indication).

Time division multiplex (TDM) remote control system

The Class 90s are equipped with a remote control system similar to that on the Glasgow-Edinburgh push-pull trains, using the two lighting wires – termed Railway Clearing House (RCH) cables – fitted to all BR's passenger-carrying locomotive-hauled coaches. The TDM system avoids the need for expensive dedicated cables for remote control purposes (40 or so are used on wired systems like multiple-unit trains). The Scottish trains are composed of a rake of Mk 3 coaches powered by a Class 47/7 locomotive controlled from a remote driving trailer.

The Class 90 is designed to operate in a similar push-pull manner with a streamlined Driving Van Trailer (DVT), styled to match the locomotive. A total of 52 are being built by BREL for push-pull services on the WCML.

TDM works on the principle that if time is divided into accurate 'time divisions', it is possible to send different control signals along the same pair of wires one after another, allocating each signal a different time slot, called a 'channel'. There are over 50 channels in the Class 90 system. The system is a bit like using a single line to pass a series of trains at discrete, strictly controlled time intervals.

The same RCH cables also carry two speech circuits 'piggyback' style, one for the public address system and the other for driver/guard communication.

Thus the driver is able to operate the Class 90 by remote control from the DVT driving desk which has a control layout identical in most respects to that fitted to the new locomotives.

The Class 90 will also be able to work with IC225 Mk 4 ECML stock using 12-way UIC cables instead of the RCH connections.

'InterCity 225'

Below:
Class 91 'A' side interior equipment

Bottom:
Class 91 'B' side interior equipment

Introduction

IC225 is an acronym for 'InterCity 225', a brand name for the 140mph (225kmh) Class 91 Bo-Bo electric locomotive that is the new flagship of BR's ac electrified InterCity routes and will power its nine-coach train push-pull style, marshalled between the Class 91 and a matching DVT.

The Class 91 is the most important — and exciting — traction and rolling stock development of the decade. This new 6,075hp (continuous) locomotive is around the same size as a Class 87 and is BR's fastest and most powerful ac electric locomotive. Designed by GEC Transportation Projects (the main contractor), the locomotive is equipped with GEC electrical equipment while the mechanical parts and final assembly were subcontracted to BREL at its Crewe locomotive works.

This, 'superloco' has a number of high-tech features that will appeal to readers interested in microcomputers. It uses a 16-bit computer to control its four body-mounted, separately excited (SEPEX) traction motors, each producing 1,518hp and easily the most powerful ever used on a British traction unit.

Each traction motor drives its associated wheelset with a unique transmission system using bevel gears and a universally jointed shaft with an arrangement similar to that used in rear drive motor vehicles.

Fig 55

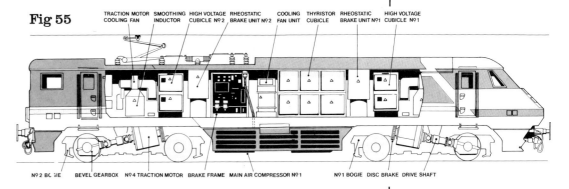

TRACTION MOTOR COOLING FAN · SMOOTHING INDUCTOR · HIGH VOLTAGE CUBICLE № 2 · RHEOSTATIC BRAKE UNIT № 2 · COOLING FAN UNIT · THYRISTOR CUBICLE · RHEOSTATIC BRAKE UNIT № 1 · HIGH VOLTAGE CUBICLE № 1

№ 2 BOGIE · BEVEL GEARBOX · № 4 TRACTION MOTOR · BRAKE FRAME · MAIN AIR COMPRESSOR № 1 · № 1 BOGIE · DISC BRAKE · DRIVE SHAFT

Fig 56

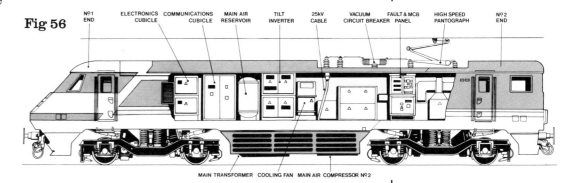

№ 1 END · ELECTRONICS CUBICLE · COMMUNICATIONS CUBICLE · MAIN AIR RESERVOIR · TILT INVERTER · 25kV CABLE · VACUUM CIRCUIT BREAKER · FAULT & MCB PANEL · HIGH SPEED PANTOGRAPH · № 2 END

MAIN TRANSFORMER · COOLING FAN · MAIN AIR COMPRESSOR № 2

Right:
Class 91 interior layout

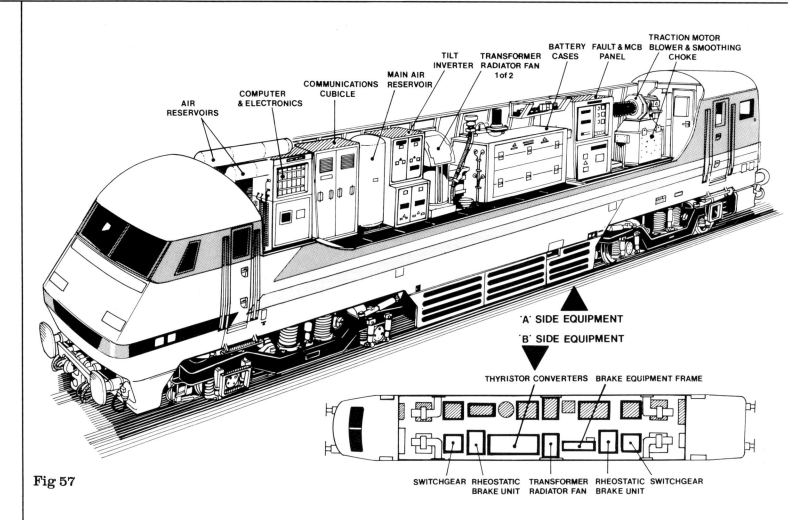

AIR
RESERVOIRS

COMPUTER
& ELECTRONICS

COMMUNICATIONS
CUBICLE

MAIN AIR
RESERVOIR

TILT
INVERTER

TRANSFORMER
RADIATOR FAN
1 of 2

BATTERY
CASES

FAULT & MCB
PANEL

TRACTION MOTOR
BLOWER & SMOOTHING
CHOKE

'A' SIDE EQUIPMENT

'B' SIDE EQUIPMENT

THYRISTOR CONVERTERS   BRAKE EQUIPMENT FRAME

SWITCHGEAR   RHEOSTATIC
BRAKE UNIT

TRANSFORMER
RADIATOR FAN

RHEOSTATIC
BRAKE UNIT

SWITCHGEAR

Fig 57

Microcomputer

The traction microcomputer is programmable, its
instructions being held in solid-state erasable
programmable read-only memories (EPROMs). Such
devices, well known to computer buffs, are fitted inside the
plug-in programme cartridges used by some home
computers. The performance data is held in a random
access memory (RAM). Automatic self-diagnosis (fault
logging) facilities are provided to aid the maintenance
engineer and the locomotive is also equipped with speed
preselection.

Like the Class 89, the '91s' have speed measurement
using Doppler radar for the wheel creep control. This
system maximises tractive effort when starting a train
under difficult operating conditions.

Endurance trials

The first 10 Class 91 locomotives are now in service; these
will carry out endurance and other trials with some high
speed running at 140mph or more. King's Cross to Leeds
services will be the first to see the locomotives in
revenue-earning service. When this first batch have

performed satisfactorily (each one will average some 420,000km/year), a second batch will be delivered in 1990-91 ready to work high speed passenger trains to Newcastle and Edinburgh following completion of the ECML electrification in 1992.

The way forward

IC225 is the result of a strategic review of InterCity future train options for ac electrified routes which established that a high speed train using a detachable locomotive would provide the most cost-effective way forward. Investigations showed that the alternatives were more costly; a unitary train had a number of operational disadvantages and lacked flexibility, while a second option, using two HST-style power cars, was an expensive way to buy performance, it also meant duplicating all the traction equipment.

The new locomotive would need to satisfy a basic InterCity requirement to haul or propel a 600-tonne train at a maximum of 140mph during daytime operation, and at night, with West Coast operation in mind, take a 15-car, 830-tonne sleeping car train (with a 100mph maximum) speed) over the heavy gradients at Shap, Beattock and elsewhere. The locomotive would also have to cope with emergency operating conditions and be able to restart these heavy trains on the steepest gradients if halted by signals.

Tenders were invited from a number of manufacturers for the supply of 31 locomotives intended for service on the ECML, BR's second busiest InterCity route. The £35 million contract, part of the £306 million electrification from London to Leeds and Edinburgh, was awarded to GEC/BREL in 1986 and thus was born the Class 91 'Electra' locomotive. BR has an option on a further 25 units for the WCML, which, if exercised, will bring faster running to BR's busiest InterCity network.

Left:
Class 91 cab, showing the driver's controls.

Assembly lines

At its Crewe locomotive works BREL laid down a new Class 91 production line alongside an identical one for the Class 90, now in service on the WCML. These two lines, assembling in one place two quite different ac electric locomotives, are unique in BR history.

Automobile-style assembly techniques have been introduced for the first time for both the Class 90 and the Class 91, using the principle of 'just in time' manufacturing, making the stockpiling of components unnecessary. Parts are timed for delivery by the supplier in

Below:
Class 91, Mk 4 coach and DVT formation for ECML services

Class 91 ELECTRA locomotive   Mark 4 day coaches   Driving van trailer

Fig 58

step with the construction of the locomotive on the production line.

GEC has also introduced another first in traction design by building a skeletal Class 91 complete with traction motors but minus its mechanical and structural parts for static test purposes at its Preston works. Testing takes place under the control of a computer which can make the 'locomotive' simulate a complete journey from London to Edinburgh at speeds of up to 140mph. This gives the engineers a rare opportunity to witness the locomotive's performance on a real, rather than a theoretical, basis with the advantage that any gremlins in the circuitry or elsewhere can be removed on the factory floor.

The Class 91 is gradually displacing the diesel IC125s which currently operate most InterCity services on the ECML. Initially, the locomotives replaced one of the Class 43 IC125 power cars with the other under power and providing the non-standard three-phase train supply. This temporary arrangement — a consequence of success, with the ECML electrification running so far ahead of schedule — has given extra proving mileage under Class 91 power and will last until enough Metro-Cammell Mk 4 coaches have been delivered.

A Class 91 has a peak output of 4,700kW (6,300hp) at the rail, and with an overall designed maximum speed of 240km/hr (149mph) 'Electra' will be BRs fastest electric locomotive. There are no plans for it to exceed 200km/hr (125mph) for the time being.

Lower centre of gravity

An outline drawing of the IC225 concept shows the push-pull principle; the locomotive, however, is always at the north end of the train. The profile drawing illustrates a side view of the locomotive. Its most striking feature is a streamlined nose at one end and a blunt end at the other, an asymmetric configuration designed to integrate the locomotive more closely with its train. Two driving compartments are provided, one at each end; with the blunt end leading, the locomotive is restricted to 100mph.

The Class 91 has its internal electrical equipment arranged on either side of a central corridor, with the main transformer mounted externally under the floor. Putting the main transformer, the twin air compressors and the four body-mounted traction motors low down lowers the centre of gravity, thereby minimising body roll and pantograph movement.

The way 'Electra' works (outlined in Fig 59 for the benefit of readers unfamiliar with ac electrics) is identical to all other electrics except in some points of detail. The pantograph (**1**) collects traction current at 25kV ac from the overhead live wires. This is passed via a vacuum circuit breaker (**2**) and cable (**3**) to the main transformer primary winding (**4**), then to axle brushes (**5**), the wheels and the running rails (**6**) connected to feeder station (**7**). This is the basic electrical circuit between the feeder station and the locomotive.

The alternating current flowing in the primary winding (**4**) induces an alternating current to flow in the main transformer traction secondary winding (**8**) but at a lower voltage, around 1,000V. Thus, the transformer steps down the voltage of the overhead wires and the current in the secondary winding is led by cables to microcomputer-controlled thyristor converters (**9**).

A thyristor is a solid-state semiconductor device with no moving parts; a close relative of the diode which, as the technically minded will know, can be used in various combinations to convert alternating current (ac) to direct

Key to Fig 59
1. Pantograph
2. Vacuum circuit breaker
3. Supply cable
4. Transformer primary winding
5. Axle brushes
6. Running rails for return current
7. Feeder station
8. Transformer secondary winding
9. Thyristor convertors
10. Traction motor
11. Control circuits

Below:
How 'Electra' works

Fig 59

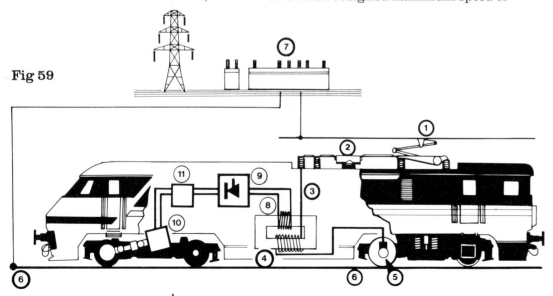

current (dc). When used in the traction circuitry they can be made to vary the output voltage from the main transformer (and convert this output to dc) for the traction motors (**10**) to control their speed and power in step with the driver's demand for power. The thyristor therefore replaces the complex electromechanical tap changer fitted to BR's first-generation ac locomotives, performing the same variable voltage traction motor control function.

The thyristors work by switching the power supply to the motors on and off very rapidly, as fast as 100 times a second. For example, at low speeds the switching rate is such that the thyristors spend more time switched off than on, effectively the output voltage from the transformer is reduced and the motors revolve slowly. If, on the other hand, more power is required, the switching rate is increased and the thyristors spend a higher proportion of their time switched on rather than off. The secondary winding transformer output voltage therefore rises, and with it the speed of the motors. In this way, movements of the driver's power controller handle are translated into dc output voltages to produce the required current in the four dc motors that drive the wheels.

The thinking locomotive

Traction power needs to be controlled effectively so that the train can be started gently from rest without inducing wheelspin (when the wheels lose their grip), and then gradually worked up to full power. The trick is to apply power right up to the point where further increases will induce wheelspin. Such tricks are kept in the microcomputer's memory bank which tells the control system the correct thyristor switching rate for the load and the driver's demand for power. The Class 91's power control system is therefore notchless — and almost infinitely variable — and this gives the locomotive the ability to perform on steeply graded routes with a heavy train in tow without slipping to a standstill, or to accelerate quickly back to line speed after a restriction, or from a station stop.

'Electra' has separately excited (SEPEX) motors, the description given to a design of motor with its stationary field windings (which encircle the motor armature and make it revolve) fed with current from a different set of

Left:
No 91001, showing the 'blunt' end. Even with this end leading 100mph running is permitted.

thyristors to those supplying current to the rotating armature. This gives them considerable automatic anti-slip properties. But to provide complete control of the motors, particularly when rail conditions and adhesion are at their worst, a speed signal independent of wheel rotation is required in case all the wheels slip together. 'Electra' has a Doppler radar speedometer for this purpose, and speed probes on each of the motors so the computer can tell if wheelslip is taking place, which axle is the culprit, and take action to correct it if it is excessive. This kind of selective control avoids the need to reduce current to all motors, something a tap changer has to do, and which reduces tractive effort from all motors rather than take individual control of the slipping axle.

Rapid acceleration can also cause wheelslip. Putting on the power affects a locomotive just the same as a high performance car, which tends to sit back on its wheels, reducing the load on those at the front and making them likely to slip. The computer takes this weight transfer into account and reduces the power very slightly to the leading motors and increases it by a small margin to the trailing ones to leave the net power unaltered.

From the driver's point of view the computer makes his job a great deal easier, particularly when rail conditions are at their worst. Instead of having continually to adjust the power controller setting to prevent wheelslip, the driver will simply select the required power and leave the locomotive to get on with it. Only when wheelslip is prolonged or serious will the driver reduce power.

The computer also controls the dynamic (electric rheostatic) brakes, protects the motors from overload and, with the maintenance engineer in mind, logs traction faults and remembers them for future analysis. The computer (an Intel 8086 16-bit device) 'talks' to the remote control system from the DVT and performs most of the former mechanical interlocks in the control circuitry of conventional locomotives.

Thus, the new Class 90 and 91 units will become the first 'thinking' locomotives in service on BR!

Turning the wheels

One feature of the Class 91 which has attracted a great deal of attention is the design of its transmission; the drive from the traction motors to the wheels. Here, the Class 91 follows the APT principle of body-mounted motors driving the axles via universally-jointed driveshafts and final drive 'gearboxes', DMU style.

Where the Class 91 design departs from the APT is in the location of the motors themselves. These are arranged side by side, below and mounted on the body between the bogie sideframes, occupying the space normally taken up by conventional bogie-mounted motors. The final drive (bevel) gearboxes are themselves fully suspended from the bogie, with unique, GEC-designed flexible drives linking them to the axles which pass through the centre of the gearbox with enough clearance to give freedom of movement.

This innovation is a response to some of the problems associated with high speed running. The load imposed by the wheels varies as they pass over irregularities in the track, the forces due to the load increasing as the speed rises. Research has shown that at high speeds these forces are very great and damage the track severely. To reduce them, the designers were obliged to make corresponding reductions in vehicle weight if possible, or to reduce the unsprung mass of the wheels and the suspension elements.

The term 'unsprung weight' refers to the dead weight of the axle and any mass attached to it. Such a mass is not cushioned by springs and quite literally 'hammers' the track at rail joints, points, crossings and track irregularities.

Most Class 86 electric locomotives and all diesel locomotives and multiple-unit trains have their motors fitted inside the bogie frame, driving the axle through reduction spur gears. The motor is actually 'axle hung', being suspended at one end from the bogie frame and at the other on bearings mounted on the axle itself. Thus the axle supports half the weight of the traction motor plus its own weight and that of the axleboxes, etc. Though the unsprung mass is considerable, when used on trains with low axleloads and relatively small motors — like multiple-units — the track forces can be tolerated because speeds do not normally exceed 100mph. Such a system, however, used on Class 86 locomotives with 20-tonne axleloads and large, heavy motors, coupled with sustained 100mph operation, caused considerable track damage to the WCML when they were first introduced. The Class 86 fleet has now been modified to make the locomotives kinder to the track.

One way to reduce unsprung weight is to hang the motors on the bogie frame completely, a solution to one problem which brings others in its wake. The motors are now rigid, do not move with the axles on the suspension, and therefore need the complication of a flexible drive system to take care of the misalignment that takes place between the motor, the driving gears and the axle when the train moves on its suspension.

Classes 87, 90 and Class 43 IC125 power cars solve this problem very neatly with an ingenious system of driveshafts connected to the motor armature at one end and passing through its hollow centre, to emerge at the other end where it drives an axle-mounted reduction gearset which in turn drives the wheels.

With such a transmission, an IC125 reduces the unsprung mass so that track forces at 125mph are actually below those imposed by existing 100mph trains. All these rules apply equally to the Class 91, which has an even higher performance than the IC125. Its transmission system is shown in Fig 60 A-D. Note that the axle passes freely through the quill tube (which drives it) and the gearbox casing. Readers familiar with Class 87 locomotives will quickly latch on to the fact that its motor driveshaft

Fig 60

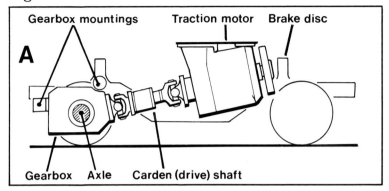

A
Gearbox mountings — Traction motor — Brake disc
Gearbox — Axle — Carden (drive) shaft

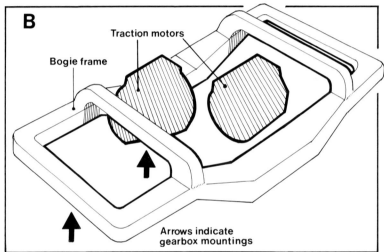

B
Traction motors
Bogie frame
Arrows indicate gearbox mountings

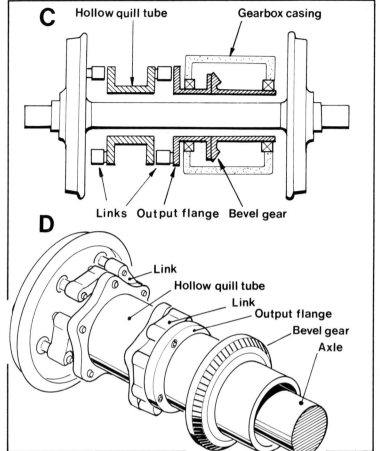

C
Hollow quill tube — Gearbox casing
Links — Output flange — Bevel gear

D
Link
Hollow quill tube
Link
Output flange
Bevel gear
Axle

Left:
Class 91 transmission system.

principle has been transferred from the motor to the axle on the Class 91, the fully suspended gearbox sitting where the motor armature would be located. With this design, clever engineering has reduced the unsprung weight to a little over 1.7 tonnes, slightly more than the weight of an individual wheelset and half the weight of the flexible coupling. Considering the complexity of the drive, this is quite an achievement.

Each of the motors is fitted with an inboard disc brake, replacing the conventional tread brake used on other locomotives. This will be used at slow speeds when the rheostatic braking effect from the motors falls off, or in an emergency.

Left:
Class 91 'Electra' No 91001 is seen here on the day of its roll-out to the press, 12 February 1988.

Pacers and Sprinters

Introduction

This section shows together BR's Pacer and Sprinter trains. All are now in service with others planned for introduction as part of BR's £55 million re-equipment plan for Provincial's countrywide network.

Pacers

Pacer trains (Classes 141, 142, 143 and 144) are lightweight DMUs that have been introduced to replace older conventional DMUs scheduled for replacement. The trains were originally introduced in two-car form, each two-axle car a little over 15m long and individually powered by a Leyland 218bhp diesel engine driving, originally, through a Self Changing Gears automatic gearbox to one axle at the inner end. The engines are turbocharged, providing rapid acceleration to a maximum speed of 75mph. Pacers have power-operated folding doors, toilets and attractive interior decor.

There are three vehicle types: a DMS(L), an operators code for a Driver Motor Standard with a lavatory, a DMS, identical to the DMS(L) but without the toilet compartment, and, introduced for West Yorkshire Class 144s, an MS Centre-coach. The term 'driver', incidentally, refers to a driving compartment, whilst 'motor' can be any kind of power unit, electric or diesel.

The Class 141 was originally incompatible with all other Pacers. It is narrow bodied, with 94 seats arranged in a 2+2 configuration, and has other external differences compared with its Class 142 successor. Class 141s originally had a Tightlock semi-automatic coupler with external jumper cables and air hoses, and a simplified version of the PBL automatic air brake first seen on the Class 58 freight locomotive. This equipment has now been removed and replaced with Provincial-standard BSI couplers and three-step electropneumatic brakes. The '142s', '143s' and '144s' have conventional 3+2 seating. They are equipped with Westcode-type three-step automatic air brakes and BSI fully automatic couplers which make all the necessary electrical and pneumatic connections between units when operating in multiple-unit formations. The coupler is remotely operated by push buttons from the driver's desk.

The Class 142 has basically the same Leyland National bus body components as the Class 141 but with detail differences, most notably a wider body built to normal railway dimensions to accommodate 122 passengers. The front end design is much neater, the lack of external pipes and connections making the Class 142 a most attractive unit altogether.

Sprinter 150

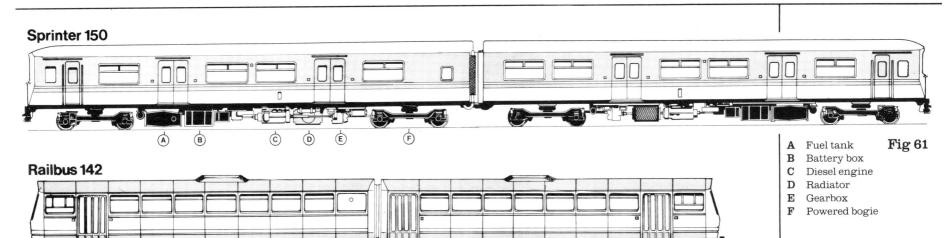

Railbus 142

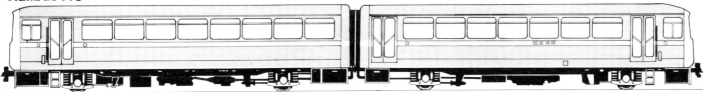

Railbus 143

A Fuel tank **Fig 61**
B Battery box
C Diesel engine
D Radiator
E Gearbox
F Powered bogie

Left:
Sprinter and Pacer exterior layouts compared

Below:
Class 150/1 two-car Sprinter DMU.

Class 141

Number of trains: 40
Builder: BREL/Leyland
Coupler: Tightlock semi-automatic
Brake system: D&M APB(a) automatic air operated
General information: Narrow bodied (bus width) bodies with 2+2 seating, capacity 94 passengers. In service in West Yorkshire. Colour scheme: all in West Yorkshire PTE red and cream.

Class 142

Number of trains: 50
Builder: ART (BREL/Leyland)
Coupler: BSI fully automatic
Brake system: Westcode type three-step automatic, air operated
General information: For Greater Manchester and Provincial Network North-West services. Has seating capacity of 122. Colour scheme: Greater Manchester units are painted orange, white and brown; remainder Provincial Sector light blue with white and dark blue stripes.

Class 143

Number of trains: 25
Builder: Walter Alexander/Andrew Barclay
Coupler: BSI fully automatic
Brake system: Westcode type three-step automatic, air operated
General information: All 122-seat Class 143 trains operate in and around Tyneside. Colour scheme: Six Pacers are in Tyne & Wear PTE white and yellow; the rest are in Provincial light/dark blue and white livery.

Class 144

Number of trains: 23
Builder: Walter Alexander/BREL
Coupler: BSI fully automatic
Brake system: Westcode type three-step automatic, air operated
General information: For service in West Yorkshire and Humberside. 122 seats. Colour scheme: West Yorkshire red and cream.

Right:
Close-up of the Voith gearbox.

Sprinter Class 150/1 and 150/2

Number of trains: 135
Builder: BREL, York
Coupler: BSI fully automatic
Brake system: Westcode-type three-step air operated
Seating capacity: 138
Colour scheme: Provincial light/dark blue livery

Scottish coachbuilder Walter Alexander built the bodies for the Class 143 and 144 trains. BREL built the underframes for all the trains except the Class 143. This has a Scottish-built underframe by Andrew Barclay, Kilmarnock. Up to four compatible Pacer units can be coupled together to form eight-car trains.

Sprinters

The prototype Sprinter, Class 150/0 came from BREL's EMU production line at York, originally in three-car form using modified Class 455 EMU bodyshells, each with a single underfloor diesel engine. Another pair of three-car prototypes, Class 151, came from Birmingham builder Metro-Cammell.

BR's first production Sprinter was the Class 150/1, basically a two-car version of the Class 150/0 prototype. This was followed by the Class 150/2 variant with detail differences which included power operation of all the doors (Class 150/1 had a pair of hinged doors behind each driving compartment) and a full gangway connection at both ends to permit through passenger access between coupled Class 150/2 units. A total of 50 Class 150/1 trains and 85 150/2 trains are in service.

Like their new EMU counterparts, the Class 150s have air suspension, public address equipment and power-operated doors. Each car has a single turbocharged 285bhp Cummins diesel engine driving through a Voith automatic transmission to Gmeinder final drives fitted to both axles of the inner bogie. This combination has proved very successful in service and was standardised on later builds, including the Classes 155 and 156 in Fig 63.

Fig 62   Class 150 Sprinter builds compared

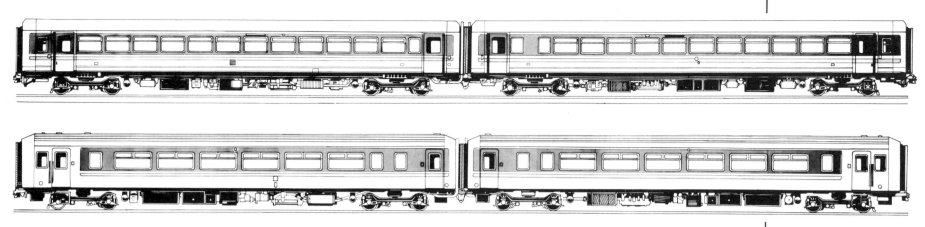

Fig 63 Class 155 and 156 Super Sprinters compared

The Leyland Bus-designed and built Class 155 two-car DMUs were BR's first units with longer (and slightly narrower) 23m cars, and are fitted with 2+2 seating unlike the 20m Class 150s with their 3+2 seats. Unit No 155001 was handed over by the makers at the end of April 1987. Also to the 23m length is the Metro-Cammell Class 156, which entered service later that year.

Both Classes 155 and 156 have interiors to a higher standard than the '150s'. They are equipped with special toilets designed so that the disabled can use them (with space for a wheelchair at one of the doorways) and interior sockets to provide power to catering trolleys to befit their cross-country role. New for BR was the use of single-leaf power-operated sliding/plug doors on Class 155 units. These move outwards to open and then slide along the outside of the vehicle.

Sprinters are used on longer distance routes, with the shorter hauls being reserved for the Pacers. All the production Sprinters (from Class 150/1 onwards) can run in multiple with each other and up to four units can be coupled together. Both the Class 155 and Class 156 trains are fully described in the following two sections.

Sprinter Class 155

Number of trains: 42
Builder: Leyland, Workington
Coupler: BSI fully automatic
Brake system: Westcode type three-step, air operated
Seating capacity: 160
Colour scheme: Provincial light/dark blue livery, some in West Yorkshire red and cream.

Sprinter Class 156

Number of trains: 114
Builder: Metro Cammell, Birmingham
Coupler: BSI fully automatic
Brake system: Westcode type three-step, air operated
Seating capacity: 158
Colour scheme: Provincial light/dark blue livery

Left:
The Cummins diesel engine is the subject of this photograph, showing the installation on a Class 150 series Sprinter. The turbocharger can be seen in the middle of the picture — the enormous exhaust pipe will give a clue to its position.

Super Sprinter Class 155: The Longer Look

Below:
The Class 155's airy interior showing the 23m body's spacious layout.

Below right:
Class 155 driver's controls.

The Leyland Bus-designed and built Class 155 Sprinter was BR's first DMU with longer 23m cars. With the exception of the bogies, Leyland manufactured the complete train itself, unlike the 232 Pacer cars in Classes 141 and 142 which were a co-operative venture with BREL. For the Class 155 (and the Metro-Cammell Class 156), BREL has supplied all the bogies.

The Class 155 is a very attractive train indeed with a particularly neat front end. Its increased length (compared with conventional DMUs) is something that is not immediately obvious until the wide picture windows are counted; there are 11 of them, all closely spaced. This extra dimension enhances the proportions of the train, giving it a Continental look while the power-operated doors fitting snugly into the bodysides add to this impression. The doors are of a sliding plug design but with a single leaf (another first on BR), and move outwards from the door opening before sliding along the outside of the coach. Each door is suspended on links and pivoting rods hidden from view. Passenger door control buttons are also provided both inside and outside the train.

The bodyshell is made in two parts with a separate floorpan. The latter is then combined with the body to form an integrally-constructed coach of immense strength. Inside, the new Sprinter '155' is bright and airy, using a red and grey colour scheme that echoes the interior of InterCity's refurbished Mk 3 stock. The seats incorporate miniature fold-down snack tables and are arranged in a 2+2 configuration.

With more windows than earlier Sprinter types there is not so much conflict with seat spacing – something that is doubtless appreciated by passengers on scenic routes. In the centre of the vehicle, however, the seats are in facing pairs with a full-size table between them, a useful feature for passengers travelling on business. A trolley catering service is provided on some journeys, the trolley being plugged into a special socket.

Like all Sprinters, the '155s' have air suspension, air brakes and public address equipment. There is also a separate lockable parcels compartment in one of the cars

while the other has a toilet specially designed for access by the disabled. Full passenger access between coupled Class 155 trains is provided using BREL-built gangways.

Mechanically the trains are identical to the production builds of Class 150 trains, with Cummins turbocharged 285bhp engines driving both axles of the inner bogies via Voith gearboxes and Gmeinder final drives. Fig 64 shows the final drive layout. Some of the bogie equipment has been omitted for clarity.

A total of 84 coaches has been delivered. All were originally allocated to Cardiff and Leeds for operating a number of through services to Crewe via Hereford and the West Country, while some diagrams take them to Bristol, Salisbury, Southampton and Portsmouth. Cardiff to Birmingham via Gloucester and Worcester services, and their use on some services from Worcester to Oxford, also bring Sprinter '155s' to the Midlands. The West Yorkshire units are used on local PTE services.

The trains have brought cross-country services right up to date with greatly improved standards of passenger comfort and amenity. They have a quiet ride, and with noticeably quicker acceleration than their first-generation counterparts, can provide a better service. Their 75mph maximum speed is no handicap on most Provincial routes; for still higher speeds the new Super Sprinter '158' will be available.

Fig 64

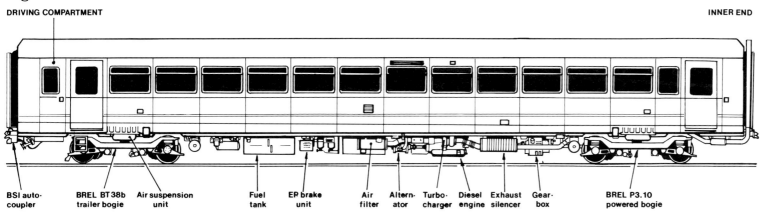

DRIVING COMPARTMENT — INNER END

BSI auto-coupler | BREL BT38b trailer bogie | Air suspension unit | Fuel tank | EP brake unit | Air filter | Altern-ator | Turbo-charger | Diesel engine | Exhaust silencer | Gear-box | BREL P3.10 powered bogie

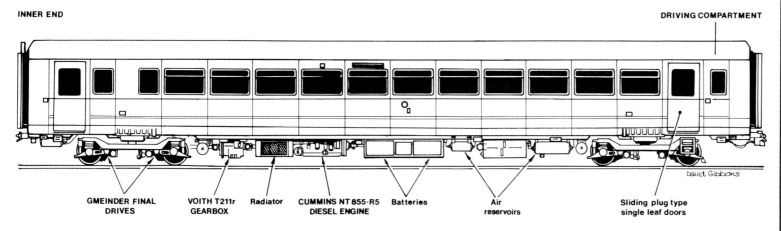

INNER END — DRIVING COMPARTMENT

GMEINDER FINAL DRIVES | VOITH T211r GEARBOX | Radiator | CUMMINS NT 855·R5 DIESEL ENGINE | Batteries | Air reservoirs | Sliding plug type single leaf doors

David Gibbons

Left:
Super Sprinter profile: the Class 155

Super Sprinter Class 156

Bringing a new look to cross-country services

The Metro-Cammell Class 156 Super Sprinters, now in service on the Anglia Region, have spearheaded a revised network of services from East Anglia to the West Midlands and the Northwest of England since 1988.

The Class 155 Super Sprinters entered service in Scotland in October 1988, their schedules taking them from Glasgow to the Scottish Highlands and Stranraer. Later, Provincial's revamped services will enter a new phase of expansion when higher specification Class 158, 90mph, air-conditioned 'Express' units are introduced on the Glasgow and Edinburgh to Aberdeen services. They will also replace locomotive-hauled trains on the Newcastle-Liverpool Trans-Pennine service.

Their introduction will also bring other changes to the network, and Super Sprinters will eventually be redeployed on services from Manchester to Blackpool. Passengers in mid-Wales and on the Cambrian Coast will also see them in service.

This £300 million re-equipment of the Provincial Sector with new trains represents a massive investment to take it into the 21st century.

Worlds apart from older DMUs

The Metro-Cammell-designed Class 156, 75mph DMU was assembled in the company's Washwood Heath plant in Birmingham from where a total of 228 cars has been delivered.

Below:
Super Sprinter profile: the Class 156

Fig 64B

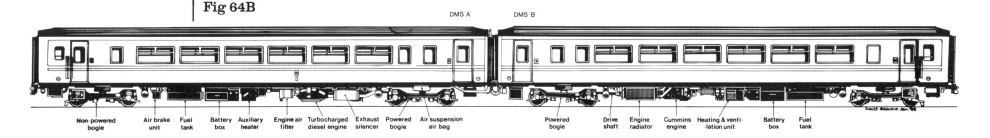

DMS 'A'   DMS 'B'

Non-powered bogie | Air brake unit | Fuel tank | Battery box | Auxiliary heater | Engine air filter | Turbocharged diesel engine | Exhaust silencer | Powered bogie | Air suspension air bag | Powered bogie | Drive shaft | Engine radiator | Cummins engine | Heating & ventilation unit | Battery box | Fuel tank

Left:
This picture clearly shows the more rounded profile of the Metro-Cammell Class 156 compared to the Class 155 design.

Class 156 trains are in two-car form with a pair of Driving Motor Standard (DMS) vehicles coupled back to back. Both cars are identical except in points of detail. The DMS(A) vehicle has a toilet, specially designed for disabled passengers (see the Super Sprinter floorplan), opposite which is a space for a wheelchair. The DMS(B) is not equipped with a toilet and instead has a lockable, secure parcels area. Unusually for a BR multiple-unit, the toilet is immediately behind the driving compartment.

Seating for a total of 150 passengers is provided in airline-style seats, incorporating fold-down snack tables. Some of the seats are arranged in facing pairs with a full-sized table between them, a feature much appreciated by business travellers or familes with children.

Wide picture windows help to produce a bright and airy interior, heightened by a very attractive colour scheme in Provincial's 'house style' of red and grey, identical to that used on the Leyland Bus Class 155. Catering trolleys can be used; these plug into a special socket at each end of the cars.

Heating is thermostatically controlled, utilising waste heat from the engine cooling system, supplemented by an oil-fired heater on the underframe. This is connected to floor-level grilles along the bodyside interior. The boiler will also preheat the diesel engine to make it easier to start at low temperatures.

Power-operated sliding doors are provided, passenger-controlled by push buttons when released from the conductor's door control panel. Like their electric counterparts, the conductor's panel on all Sprinters will close any doors left open by passengers before the train can power away from a standstill.

Mechanically, the trains are identical to Sprinter '150s', each two-car set having a pair of turbocharged 285bhp

Fig 65

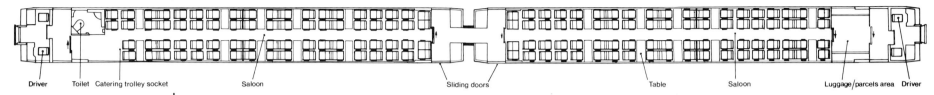

DMS 'A'   DMS 'B'

Driver   Toilet   Catering trolley socket   Saloon   Sliding doors   Table   Saloon   Luggage/parcels area   Driver

Above:
Super Sprinter floorplan

Above right:
Class 156 interior.

Right:
Close-up of the Class 156's
front end.

Cummins diesel engines each driving both axles of the inner bogies via Voith turbo transmissions (basically a form of automatic gearbox and Gmeinder final drive units. This highly reliable combination has been a major success on Sprinter trains. The drawing shows the driveline configuration.

Multiple working

Class 156 trains have air suspension, three-step, load-variable braking (using the air suspension pressure to measure the load) and public address equipment. They have BSI fully-automatic couplers at each end, making the Super Sprinters compatible with any other BSI coupler-equipped trains. End gangways give full passenger access between coupled units.

BREL manufactured all the bogies for both the Class 156 and the '155' Leyland units. These are identical to those fitted to other Sprinters and have rubber primary suspension between the wheels and the bogies with self-levelling air suspension bags forming the secondary suspension supporting the body on the bogies. The bogie design is similar to that on current EMU builds but the centre portion is cranked to accommodate the driveshafts linking the two driven axles (see drawing).

Passengers will confirm they are very quiet and ride very smoothly, their rapid acceleration putting them in a different league from the noisy and slow first-generation counterparts.

Sprinters and Super Sprinters also have maintenance-saving advantages which help to make them very cost-effective trains to operate. When the new 'Provincial Express' units enter service, the re-equipment of BR's Provincial network will be almost complete.

How Sprinters and Pacers Work

Introduction

The classic British DMU train exists in one, two, three and four-car form, each powered vehicle driving the inner axle of its bogie through bus-type gearboxes and fitted with underfloor horizontal engines based closely on automotive practice. A typical example of a motor coach is shown in Fig 66, fitted with pairs of engines and transmissions, coupled to a non-powered driving trailer (not shown).

This first generation vacuum-braked train should be compared with a Sprinter Class 150 unit, illustrated in cutaway form to show the equipment underneath (some has been omitted for clarity). The '150' is simpler in most respects than the complicated, multi-engined motor coach it replaces. Each Sprinter car is powered by a single turbocharged diesel engine driving both axles of one bogie through an automatic gearbox.

Most conventional DMUs were equipped with manually-operated gearboxes (only relatively few had automatic transmissions). Like his automotive counterpart, the train driver actually changed gear using a horizontal gearchange lever and a hand 'throttle', which controlled engine speed in the manner of a car's accelerator pedal.

The driver's 'commands' for a change of gear or engine speed were sent via jumper cables and sockets between coupled units. Gear changing is a noisy process, accompanied in most cases by jerky motion and mechanical 'clunks' and 'clangs'. Nowadays, with this chore done automatically, operation of the latest DMU trains is becoming more and more like their electrically-powered counterparts.

All the Sprinters have air suspension, air (not vacuum) brakes, power-operated (air) sliding doors and attractive interiors with comfortable seating. Each Sprinter car has its own engine-driven air compressor and battery-charging alternator (with associated rectifier).

Below:
A typical first-generation DMU motor coach

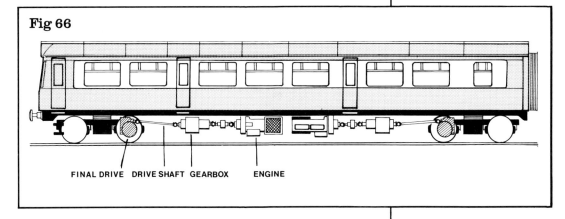

Fig 66

FINAL DRIVE   DRIVE SHAFT   GEARBOX   ENGINE

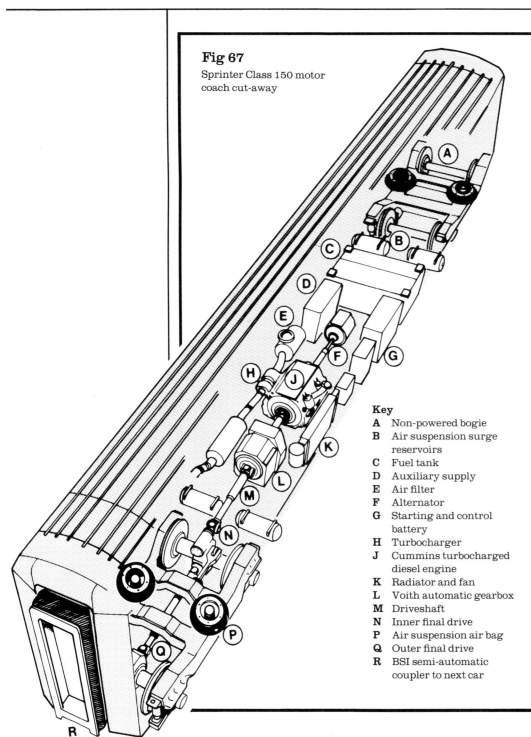

Fig 67

Sprinter Class 150 motor
coach cut-away

Key

A   Non-powered bogie
B   Air suspension surge
    reservoirs
C   Fuel tank
D   Auxiliary supply
E   Air filter
F   Alternator
G   Starting and control
    battery
H   Turbocharger
J   Cummins turbocharged
    diesel engine
K   Radiator and fan
L   Voith automatic gearbox
M   Driveshaft
N   Inner final drive
P   Air suspension air bag
Q   Outer final drive
R   BSI semi-automatic
    coupler to next car

All the latest DMUs have two batteries, one providing current for engine starting and controls, while the other powers the lights and heating equipment. Another change is in the heating system, the new trains having warm air heating using waste heat from the engine cooling system. This is supplemented by an oil-fired water heater as required.

Controlling the power

The feature on diesel locomotives explained how the power output is controlled. A master switch selects the direction of travel and a power controller sets the speed and power of the unit. This acts on the fuel system and it is the quantity of fuel injected which regulates the speed and power.

Getting the fuel into the cylinders is not so easy because at the moment the fuel is required, the pressure in the cylinders is at its highest – the injection pressure can be as much as 3 tons/in. This problem is not so difficult to overcome as may be imagined because the fuel injector has the tiniest opening to pass fuel into the engine. A simplified drawing of the fuel injection system for a Cummins engine shows the main components (see Fig 68).

Fuel is drawn from a tank by a fuel pump and passed through a filter to a set of four engine valves (also called throttle valves). This contains valves, each consisting of a fuel control orifice (basically a hole in a pipe) of different diameters which are opened electrically in different combinations. The combination (and therefore the amount of fuel passing to the injectors) is set by the power controller step (or notch) selected by the driver. The

Simplified fuel injection system

Fig 68

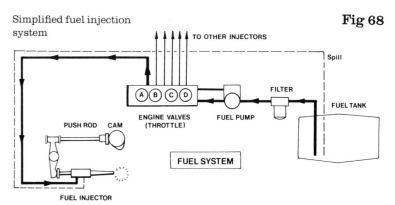

Fig 69

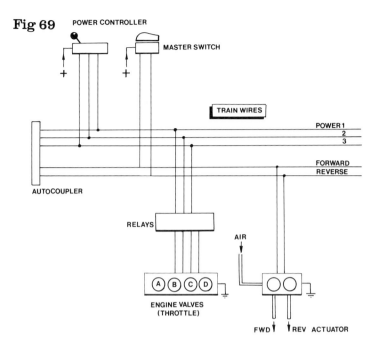

injector is opened at the right time in the operating sequence of the engine by a cam.

The engine valves are energised electrically by relays (electrical switches) which are in turn influenced by a set of three power 'train wires' running through the train from end to end (see Fig 69). The wires are connected to a seven-step power controller which energises them in different combinations to give a corresponding value of fuel from the engine valves.

Fig 70

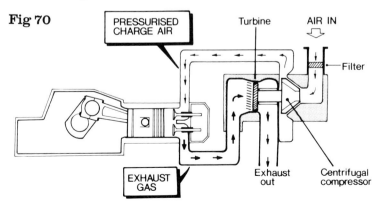

Fig 71

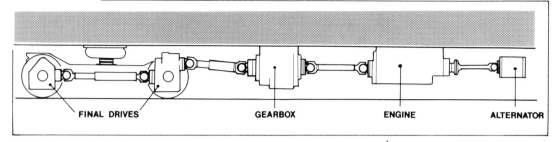

The other two wires select the direction of travel, and are connected to the automatic transmission's innards, within which is an air piston that selects forward and reverse gear.

The turbocharger

A turbocharger is now standard equipment on many high-performance cars. Most rail traction engines have used them for many years, long before the motor industry caught on to their advantages.

The drawing shows the component parts of a turbocharger. It consists of a rotating impeller – basically a bladed fan – made to turn by and mounted on the same shaft as a gas turbine (like a windmill), both the impeller and the turbine being enclosed by a circular casing. The turbine uses the heat energy in the exhaust gas, that would otherwise go to waste, to power it.

The turbocharger is essentially a device to obtain more power, working on the principle that if the air is compressed and its density increased more fuel can be burned, thus increasing the force acting on the pistons and, hence, the power of the engine. This is achieved by the fan blowing the air – called 'charge air' – into the engine.

More about engines

Fig 71 will remind the reader how the engine fits into the power transmission driveline that connects the engine to the wheels. The system for a Sprinter is shown; that for a Pacer is almost identical except that the driveline components are supplied by a different manufacturer and only one axle on each car is actually driven.

Left:
Power control system.

Above:
Class 150 Sprinter driveline.

Left:
Turbocharger basic principle

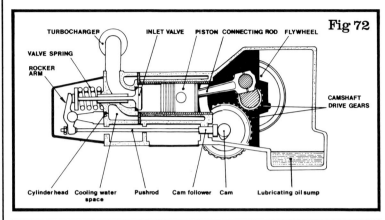

Fig 72

TURBOCHARGER   INLET VALVE   PISTON CONNECTING ROD FLYWHEEL

VALVE SPRING

ROCKER
ARM

CAMSHAFT
DRIVE GEARS

Cylinder head   Cooling water   Pushrod   Cam follower   Cam   Lubricating oil sump
space

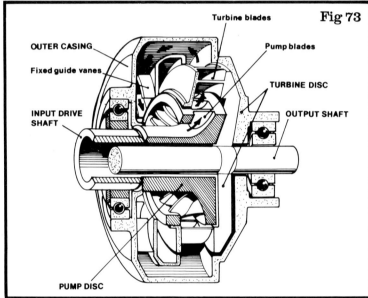

Fig 73

Turbine blades

OUTER CASING

Pump blades

Fixed guide vanes

TURBINE DISC

INPUT DRIVE
SHAFT

OUTPUT SHAFT

PUMP DISC

An elementary horizontal turbocharged diesel engine is shown in Fig 72 and highlights the mechanism for operating the inlet and exhaust valves. A pair of camshaft drive gears connected to the crankshaft together turn a camshaft running the length of the engine. This is fitted with a total of 12 cams, six inlet and six exhaust. Each cam has a 'bump' on its edge that will push to the left a cam follower that will in turn move a pushrod and rocker arm to open the appropriate valve against the tension of a spring. The spring will close the valve when the cam turns the

bump away from the cam follower. Note that only the inlet valve is shown; the exhaust valve – and all other valves – is operated in an identical manner. All the cams are arranged on the camshaft in such a way that they will each open and close the various valves at the right time in the four-stroke cycle.

The cooling water spaces have coolant circulated in them to remove unwanted heat from the engine, although some of it is used for saloon heating. An external, air-cooled radiator dissipates what remains, using a thermostatically-controlled fan which is driven by oil under pressure from an engine-driven pump. Another pump circulates lubricating oil to all the rotating (and wearing) parts of the engine through pipes and oilways formed in the engine block and within the crankshaft itself. Oil from this system gravitates back to the oil sump from where it is recirculated.

Talking about torque

Anyone learning to drive a motor car will find out very quickly that the engine has very little power when idling or at slow speed. This is particularly noticeable when starting from rest and even with the accelerator pedal pressed only gently, it is very easy to stall the engine. The ingredient that is missing is torque, another name for what is described as a turning effect, something that is very easy to understand if the reader can ride a bike. The act of turning pedals produces torque!

When starting, the pedals have to be pushed hard to make the wheels rotate but once on the move you can ease off. When you come to a hill you will need to push harder on the pedals again; in other words, more torque is required.

Much the same thing happens with a car. A gearbox, fitted in the driveline between the engine and the wheels, has internal gearwheels that multiply the engine torque at low speeds to enable the car to start. Once on the move, however, less torque (but more speed) is required, so the driver changes progressively to the next higher gear. Most cars have gearboxes with at least four forward speeds (some have five), the gearbox containing sets of gearwheels, one for each gear.

Gears are simple things to understand and most people know what they look like. If a gearwheel with only a few teeth is meshed with another with a larger number of teeth the larger one will turn more slowly – and will produce more torque – than the smaller gear. Taking this a stage further, if two meshed gears are the same size, both will turn at the same speed but in opposite directions. Thus, a gearbox has gears inside, each with different-sized gears with the correct number of teeth. These can be selected by the driver in the right combination to give the speed required. Another set is also needed to change direction.

When changing gear, it is necessary to disconnect the engine from the gearbox using a device called a clutch. The drive is taken up again when the intended gear has been selected. As every car owner will know, failure to use the clutch will cause the gearbox to make some very expensive noises!

Precisely the same equipment is needed on a diesel train, although on older units the clutch was of a different type to that fitted to the average car. The Sprinters and Pacers both have clutchless automatically-operated gearboxes, one design, Voith, fitted to all the production Sprinters, having no gears to change whatsoever (except in reverse)!

This gearbox is branded a 'turbo-transmission' by the manufacturer. Inside it has a torque converter, shown in cutaway form in Fig 73. This multiplies the torque of the engine to start the train, just like a mechanical gearbox does on a car, lorry or bus.

The torque converter therefore corresponds to the low speed (first and second) ratios while another device called a fluid coupling – basically a fluid clutch – provides a direct drive, corresponding to fourth (or top) gear for normal high speed running. Both devices are filled with oil to transmit power and when emptied, the drive from the engine to the wheels is disconnected. The control system will automatically select either the torque converter or the fluid coupling depending on the power controller notch selected by the driver and the speed of the train.

Fig 74 shows the complete gearbox in a simplified cutaway drawing (the bearings have been omitted for clarity). The imput shaft and its attached gear drives a hollow shaft fixed to an impeller inside the fluid coupling on the left, and a pump inside the torque converter on the right. With both the fluid coupling and the torque converter emptied, the gearbox will not transmit power.

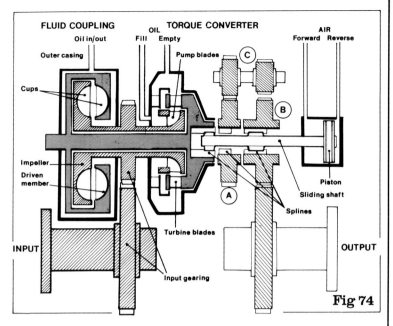

Fig 74

Left:
Gearbox cut-away view

Assuming the train is at a stand when the power controller is opened, a fill valve will automatically allow oil to enter the torque converter – see Fig 73 again. Inside it, a pump, resembling the compressor element in a turbocharger, converts the mechanical energy of the diesel engine into a flow of oil or, put another way, into energy of flow.

The oil is then converted back into mechanical energy by impinging on to the blades of a turbine arranged to rotate around the circumference of the pump. The oil then returns to the pump to begin the cycle again. The turbine is linked by the sliding shaft (see Fig 74) to the reversing gears and thence to the output shaft.

A characteristic of a torque converter is that maximum torque is produced when the turbine is at a standstill, the oil exerting a force on the turbine blades proportional to the speed of the pump. Thus, on starting, the converter multiplies torque in a way no different in principle to the selection of the low ratio first gear in a conventional mechanical gearbox. Once the turbine starts to rotate and increases speed, torque multiplication is less, similar to the effect of second (higher ratio) gear being selected, and so on.

Right:
The reversing gear mechanism

Below right:
'Pacer' style gearbox, showing sun and planet arrangement.

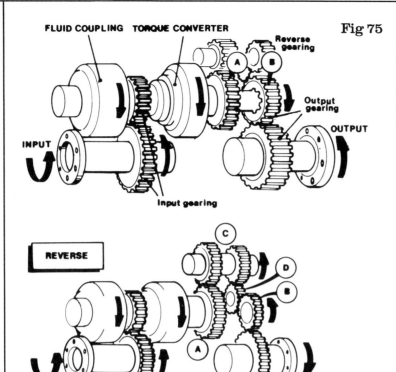

FLUID COUPLING   TORQUE CONVERTER   **Fig 75**

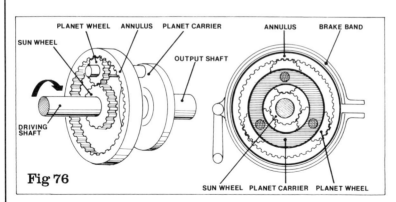

Fig 76

Finally, the train reaches a speed where torque multiplication ceases, comparable to the speed where the driver of conventional DMMU would have changed into fourth (top) gear. At this point, the control system will commence to empty the torque converter and begin to fill the adjacent fluid coupling.

A fluid coupling is composed of two elements and resembles a tennis ball cut in half with the two halves facing each other, each half containing a series of cup-shaped recesses. The engine-driven half — called an impeller — accelerates the oil, throwing it from the impeller cups into similar cups in the driven member thereby causing it to rotate. The driven member, as the drawing shows, is connected to the torque converter turbine by a shaft passing through the hollow centre of the torque converter/fluid coupling input shaft.

The emptying of the torque converter and the filling of the fluid coupling takes place smoothly and the flow of power is not interrupted. Under normal circumstances the changeover from one to the other is difficult to detect. The transmission can also freewheel in motion (just like a cycle) if the power controller is closed; a valve operates to drain both the fluid coupling and the torque converter. This will occur when the train is running on a downhill gradient, the freewheeling preventing the wheels from driving the engine into an overspeed condition. Both devices will also be drained when the power controller is closed and the train is at a standstill.

There is no direct mechanical link between the two halves of the fluid coupling or, for that matter, between the various elements inside the torque converter. The working fluid (oil) forms the only connection between the driving and driven members, the gearbox, for reasons which will now be clear, should be described as an hydraulic transmission.

Fig 75 shows how the reversing gear works. The first drawing explains what happens in forward gear when gearwheel A and the reversing geartrain are out of engagement, the drive passing through gear B only to the output shaft. In reverse, however, gear A is connected by the sliding shaft (see Fig 74) to the reversing gear. Thus, gear A meshes with gears C which in turn mesh with gear B via idler gear D, thereby reversing the direction of the output shaft.

Not that the torque converter disc and the gears A and B have internal splines (like gear teeth inside and out) which allow the sliding shaft to move laterally and at the same time make the right gear connections. The sliding shaft is moved by an air-operated piston when the driver selects the

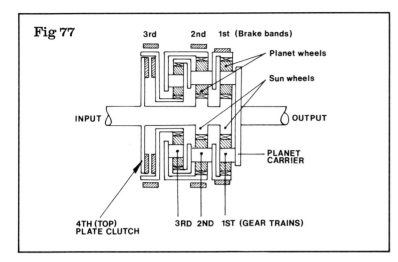

Fig 77

3rd   2nd   1st (Brake bands)

Planet wheels

Sun wheels

INPUT / OUTPUT

PLANET CARRIER

4TH (TOP) PLATE CLUTCH   3RD 2ND 1ST (GEAR TRAINS)

appropriate direction on his direction selector.

Pacer trains have a quite different gearbox, using a series of gear 'trains' that are arranged in a unique epicyclic configuration – see Fig 76, which shows the basic principle. A single geartrain consists of a driven 'sun' gearwheel around which a 'planet' gear mounted on a carrier can revolve. The planet wheel is in engagement with the sun wheel and the internal teeth of an outer 'annulus' (see the drawing on the left).

On the right of Fig 76 is a real epicyclic gear arrangement with three planet wheels (some configurations have five). Now, if the sun wheel is driven and the brake band is released, all the various gears will revolve, including the annulus. If, however, the annulus is held stationary with the brake band applied, the planet carrier itself will revolve. To make this clear, look at Fig 77 showing part of a gearbox in first gear. The first gear brake band is applied and holds the appropriate annulus stationary so that revolution of the associated sun wheel connected to the input shaft will make the first gear planets revolve to roll around the internal teeth of the annulus taking the planet carrier with them in the same direction as the input shaft but at a lower speed.

Thus, as the drawing on Fig 77 shows, it is possible to combine sets of geartrains to get the required number of speeds with the advantage that gearchanging can be accomplished without the need to move gears into (or out)

of engagement. All that is needed is to brake, or release the appropriate brake band.

Selection of the brake bands (and a plate clutch in top gear which effectively locks all the elements into a solid mass) is undertaken automatically, depending on the power notch selected by the driver, and the road speed.

Mind the doors

To complete this 'how it works' chapter, the reader will want to know how the power-operated doors work. Fig 78 explains with a drawing (greatly simplified) that shows the main parts. The endless belt is an ingenious way of making one cylinder operate two doors!

As the drawing shows, compressed air operates the doors which are electrically released by the conductor so that passengers can open and close the doors as required with push buttons mounted at each door position. The conductor's door control panel will close any doors that have been left open by passengers before the train starts. The vital door locks and interlocks have not been shown on the drawing.

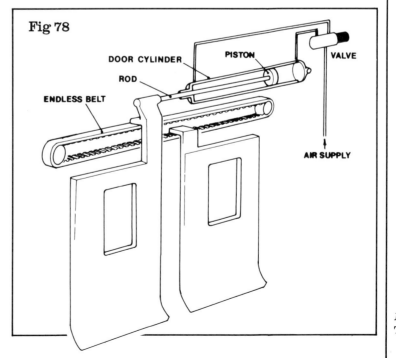

Fig 78

DOOR CYLINDER   PISTON   VALVE

ROD

ENDLESS BELT

AIR SUPPLY

Left:
'Pacer' style gearbox shown in first gear.

Left:
The door mechanism

HSTs Go Electric

Introduction

In the spring of 1988, passengers from Birmingham and Wolverhampton travelling on some West Midlands services to Euston found their train powered by a Class 43 IC125 power car with a lifeless diesel engine and a driverless Class 86 electric locomotive at the rear. 'It must be done by radio', was the standard response from the average railway enthusiast.

This unusual train formation was a specially-equipped train, performing service trials of an updated TDM remote-control system intended for future InterCity

push-pull operations on both the East Coast and West Coast main lines. The trials led the way to the introduction of even more unusual operations on the other side of the country with an IC125 train dual powered by a Class 91 ac electric locomotive and a single diesel power car with a combined power of around 8,350hp!

HST Driving Van Trailers

Two were originally converted from standard power cars for WCML development trials. These became non-powered Driving Van Trailers (DVT). Their diesel engines were

Below:
HST DVT formations

Fig 79A   Euston-West Midlands push-pull formation

HST DVT   LOCO. HAULED COACHES   CLASS 86 LOCOMOTIVE

Fig 79B   East Coast main line HST+Class 91

HST DVT   HST COACHES   CLASS 91 LOCOMOTIVE

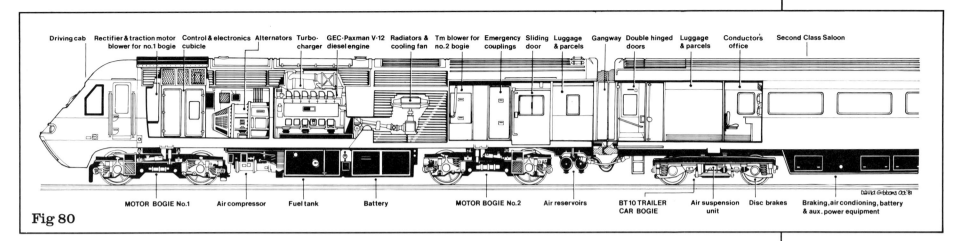

Fig 80

Labels on the figure: Driving cab · Rectifier & traction motor blower for no.1 bogie · Control & electronics cubicle · Alternators · Turbo-charger · GEC·Paxman V·12 diesel engine · Radiators & cooling fan · Tm blower for no.2 bogie · Emergency couplings · Sliding door · Luggage & parcels · Gangway · Double hinged doors · Luggage & parcels · Conductor's office · Second Class Saloon

MOTOR BOGIE No.1 · Air compressor · Fuel tank · Battery · MOTOR BOGIE No.2 · Air reservoirs · BT 10 TRAILER CAR BOGIE · Air suspension unit · Disc brakes · Braking, air condioning, battery & aux. power equipment

David Gibbons Oct '81

initially incapable of providing traction power, although they were modified to permit this. Externally, the IC125 DVTs are recognised by their standard buffers, carriage-type drawhook, air hoses and UIC jumper cable socket at the streamlined end. At the blunt end the DVT couples to the train with buckeye couplings, drawing a single-phase ETS from the adjoining coaches using standard two-pole train supply jumper cables. This is taken to a coach-type motor-alternator set in the luggage compartment, its three-phase output linked to the HST's auxiliary circuitry for control and battery-charging purposes.

The TDM equipment is housed in a cubicle next to the motor-alternator, fed from the HST's battery via a circuit breaker. Inside the driving compartment, a TDM console, with various indicator lights and push buttons, keeps the driver informed about the remote locomotive. A smaller TDM cubicle is installed behind the No 1 end driving compartment in converted electric locomotives, the equipment communicating with the DVT via RCH jumper cables at the front of the locomotive. The drawing shows the formation of one of the London Midland Region's push-pull trains. Class 86/1, 86/2, 86/4, 86/6 and 87/0 locomotives are being progressively fitted with TDM equipment.

The Class 43 power controller is modified slightly with 'soft' power notches, making it infinitely variable for ac electric operation. Inside the ac locomotive, a tractive effort translator (TET), associated TDM circuitry and traction

current measuring devices together operate the transformer tap changer which produces motor current to a level matching the Class 43's tractive effort demand, set by its power controller.

The modified power cars were later transferred to the ECML and performed mileage accumulation and driver training runs with Class 91 TDM-equipped locomotives, initially running with trains composed of sleeping cars.

Electric HSTs

With the ECML electrification running ahead of schedule and with Mk 4 coaches and DVTs still under construction, TDM-fitted IC125s have permitted electric operation until the new stock is progressively introduced into service. Thus, a number of IC125 power cars have been equipped with TDM to operate with Class 91 locomotives, the first 'electric HSTs' to operate on BR tracks.

Converted IC125s were originally intended to have their diesel engines running to produce auxiliary power for train supplies only and no tractive effort. Running experience showed, however, that the diesel engines did not take too kindly to operation for long periods at little more than tickover, the combined train supply and auxiliaries demanding only around 450hp from the 2,250hp power unit.

In the event, it was decided to let the power car produce all its rated output and service trains are actually dual

Above:
Class 43 IC125 power car cut-away

powered, with the electric locomotive and the diesel power car operating together in multiple, another first on BR! The later conversions are without the motor-alternator formerly required to allow the IC125 DVT to operate with locomotive-hauled coaches. Fig 79B shows an ECML IC125 formation.

Spotlight on the HSTs

BR's High Speed Train, or InterCity 125 (IC125), comprises two types with either seven (Class 253) or eight (Class 254) Mk 3, 23m (75.4ft) trailer vehicles marshalled between two Class 43 diesel power cars, one at each end of the train. Both types have a maximum service speed of 125mph. A seven-coach train weighs 374 tonnes and has seats for 392 passengers, while an eight-coach formation has seats for 434 passengers and weighs 409 tonnes. A single power car is 17.7m (57.9ft) long, weighs 70 tonnes, and carries 1,000gal of fuel giving a range of 1,400 miles. Route availability is 6.

The Class 43 power cars are not fitted with side buffers and standard drawgear, so special emergency drawgear has to be used to couple two trains together, or to attach a locomotive.

Both Class 253 and 254 trains are identical except in points of detail and number of trailer cars. Each power car is fitted with a single Paxman Valenta 12RP200L 12-cylinder vee-form, turbocharged and intercooled diesel engine producing 2,250bhp at 1,500rpm. A typical train will produce between 3,400 and 3,600hp at the rail, the difference between this and the installed power of 4,500hp being accounted for by the auxiliaries and the train supply. With a relatively high power-to-weight ratio, this endows a typical seven-coach train with very rapid acceleration — 66mph is achieved in 1min 39sec and 125mph in 6min 49sec.

Inside, a power car has a single, air-conditioned driving compartment at the streamlined end, an adjoining power and traction equipment area consisting of a clean air compartment, containing the main electrical equipment, and a pair of brake equipment frames. Next to this is a diesel engine compartment, a radiator compartment, a luggage compartment and, on some power cars, a former

guard's compartment at the extreme rear. The senior conductor's 'office' and a luggage compartment is located in the adjoining Trailer Guard's Second (TGS) vehicle.

The 79-litre four-stroke diesel engine is directly coupled to a main and an auxiliary alternator. The main alternator produces ac (converted to dc in a main rectifier), and this dc supply is connected to four dc traction motors. These are force-cooled and bogie-mounted, and drive the wheelsets through flexible drives to reduce the unsprung weight.

The auxiliary alternator, mounted in unit with the main alternator, produces a non-standard 415V three-phase train supply for heating, air conditioning and auxiliaries. This supply is also transformed and rectified to 110V dc for battery charging and control purposes.

Engine speed control is electric, responding to a six-position power controller with five power notches. Load regulation for the power control system is all electronic, with no moving parts, and incorporates a wheelslip detection system.

Class 253 units have the Davies & Metcalfe E70 electrically-controlled air brake system while Class 254 is fitted with Westinghouse DW2 braking equipment which is E70 compatible. The brake system gives seven steps of braking, each step selected by an electric brake controller.

Disc brakes are fitted throughout the train with additional tread brakes on the power cars. The tread brakes supplement braking effort and improve adhesion by effectively 'scrubbing' the wheel treads. The tread brake can also be operated independently by the parking brake system.

Class 43 power cars Nos 43167 to 43170 have been experimentally fitted with the Mirrlees-Blackstone MB190 diesel engine. This is a 12-cylinder vee-formation engine producing 2,400bhp at 1,500rpm. Two of these marshalled in a train together produce an electrifying performance, the train accelerating even more rapidly than normal from a standing start.

Paxman-engined power cars have a mechanically-driven radiator fan; the re-engined cars are equipped with hydraulically-powered fans using a hydrostatic pump driven off the free end of the engine. The fans are independently controlled by electronic speed control units linked to temperature probes in the appropriate system.

New Look for the West Coast: Driving Van Trailers for Push-Pull Working

Introduction

Now in service are the first of BR's high speed Driving Van Trailers (DVTs), for the WCML. These are programmed to work mainly with newly built Class 90 ac electric locomotives and Mk 2 and Mk 3 coaches on push-pull services. The locomotive hauls its train on northbound runs from Euston and propels the train south (see Fig 81). Control of the locomotive on southbound trains is from the driving compartment of the DVT, using a remote control system called TDM. Working trains in this way increases

Below:
Mk 3 DVT formation and side view

Fig 81

DRIVING VAN TRAILER　　　　　　　　　　　TRAIN　　　　　　　　　　　　　　LOCOMOTIVE

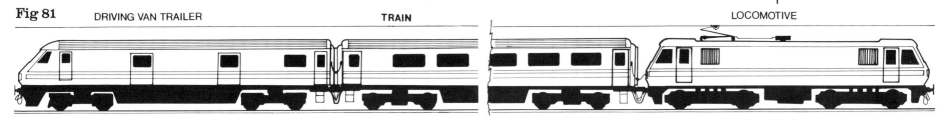

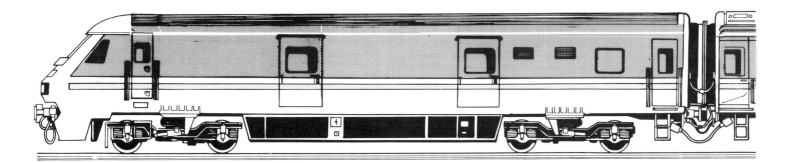

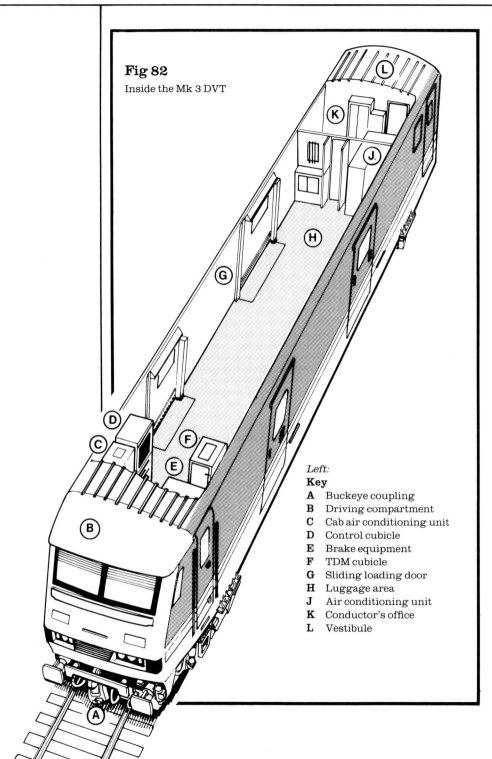

Fig 82

Inside the Mk 3 DVT

Left:

Key

A Buckeye coupling
B Driving compartment
C Cab air conditioning unit
D Control cubicle
E Brake equipment
F TDM cubicle
G Sliding loading door
H Luggage area
J Air conditioning unit
K Conductor's office
L Vestibule

terminal capacity because they can be operated like multiple-units without the need to release locomotives trapped at the buffer stops on inward services. Fewer light engine movements and a reduction in the number of locomotives required for a given service are other benefits.

Push-pull working is also being introduced on the ECML, but on this route both the coaches and the DVTs are to the new Mk 4 design, powered by 140mph Class 91 locomotives.

Mk 3-based trains and DVTs on the WCML InterCity network (BR's busiest) will be limited to a 110mph maximum, although the West Coast DVTs are capable of 125mph operation on track cleared for running at this speed.

Shaped for speed

West Coast DVTs have been designed and manufactured by BREL at Derby (Litchurch Lane) works to meet InterCity specifications. The vehicles are possibly the most attractive to leave that works in recent years, with a noticeably high standard both of construction and paint finish. The styling matches that of the Class 90 locomotive but with a sharper, Class 91 style, nose end. The vehicles weigh 44.3 tonnes, are 61.8ft long over buffers and have a carrying capacity of 8 tonnes of luggage and parcels.

At the front end DVTs are equipped with retractable buffers, a semi-automatic buckeye coupler and the usual air hose connections. The blunt (train) end has the same connections but also sports a gangway to link the vehicle to the train. Here, a vestibule and entrance doors lead from the train to an air-conditioned senior conductor's 'office' complete with desk, a superb adjustable seat identical to the driver's, public address equipment and a private communication system with the driver up front. Next to this is a spacious luggage compartment, accessed from platforms by two pairs of sliding doors on each side.

At the driving end of the luggage compartment is a small equipment bay containing the cab air conditioning, control and TDM cubicles arranged on either side of a central corridor. Also located here is a brake equipment frame with a Westinghouse braking system identical to the Class 90 locomotive.

The air-conditioned driving compartment is practically identical to that on the Class 90 locomotive. In place of the Class 90 ammeters is an LED indicator that illuminates to reassure drivers the remote locomotive is producing current in motoring or braking.

Even the Class 89/90/91 speed control system is duplicated in the DVT, giving the driver the equivalent of cruise control fitted to some expensive executive cars. The ride, too, is in the executive class, the quietness due to the absence of traction motors or power equipment on the vehicle.

Another standard fitment is a VHF train radio connecting the driver to BR's telecommunications network. The integrally-constructed all-steel bodyshell carries a number of beautifully finished glass reinforced plastic (GRP) panels, mainly at the streamlined end to form the cab, lower valance and canopy. Even the best photographs (from the photographic unit at Derby) cannot do justice to their fit and finish! A nice feature is the doors above the front lights containing the RCH jumper cables.

Bogies are to a new BREL design, called the T4 series. They have coil sprung primary suspension, yaw (anti-rotational) dampers and air secondary suspension. Power supplies come from an underframe-mounted motor alternator set, fed from the train supply. The motor alternator set charges the vehicle's standby batteries, and supplies the air-conditioning systems and other auxiliaries.

Above:
Train end of the Mk 3 DVT showing the corridor connections.

Left:
Mk 3 DVT driver's controls.

The Foster Yeoman Class 59 Diesel Locomotive

'Phenomenal'

That's what enthusiastic locomotive engineers are saying about the new American freight locomotives (BR Class 59) bought by West Country quarry firm Foster Yeoman to haul their stone trains on BR tracks.

On a test run at Foster Yeoman's Merehead quarry, No 59002 managed to lift 40 loaded 100-tonne wagons up a 1 in 25 gradient, on a curve and with a damp rail.

'Technically that means it achieved a sustained 111,000lb tractive effort at 40% adhesion, the highest output from a single locomotive recorded in this country,' claims David Russell, BR's freight engineer.

Thus reported *Railnews* in March 1986. For more details about these remarkable locomotives, read on!

Private locomotive project – the background

Foster Yeoman is BR's sixth largest freight customer with almost three-quarters of its annual output of five million tonnes of stone traffic being moved by rail. In 1984, the company spent £7 million on rail transport.

Every weekday, trains of between 2,000 and 4,600 tonnes – the largest up to a third of a mile in length and hauled (until 1986) by two Class 56 locomotives – leave Merehead, near the Western Region's West of England main line, for one of the company's distribution terminals. Many of these trains are now composed entirely of new blue and white-liveried aluminium 100-tonne bogie stone hopper wagons, each capable of carrying 9% more than the conventional steel vehicles they replaced. The company owns (or leases) a total of 300 wagons.

Foster Yeoman pioneered the marketing of Mendip limestone, and in 15 years its rail traffic has grown from nothing to around 3.5 million tonnes a year. Competition in the aggregates business is very strong, not only from other quarries (many of which send their output by road) but also from seaborne imports from Ireland and the Continent.

Foster Yeoman therefore wanted the lowest possible transport costs to maximise efficiency and counter the effects of competition. Studies carried out by the company in 1983 showed that ownership of its own locomotives would reduce these costs substantially and also produce some benefits to BR, since the locomotives released from Foster Yeoman's stone traffic would be able to take on other work. Thus was born the 'private locomotive' project and tenders were invited for the supply of the necessary locomotives from various manufacturers.

All tenders were evaluated by BRB engineers, and included the Class 56 locomotive from Brush, the Class 58 from BREL and the General Motors (GM) locomotives illustrated here. Foster Yeoman demanded a very high level of reliability and an availability figure of 95%. One of the most important contract stipulations concerned hauling power and the chosen locomotive had to be capable of moving the required trainloads single-handed.

The GM contender was alone in meeting all Foster Yeoman's requirements, including a tight delivery timescale. Furthermore, the American builder was prepared to guarantee – and demonstrate in practice – an availability of 95% on the basis of a five-day working week with maintenance being carried out at weekends. On certain routes one Class 59 can move unaided a train that would need a pair of '56s' or '58s', and this meant that with their high availability only four American locomotives would be required to move the traffic compared with 11 British ones. Commercial success meant that a fifth locomotive entered service in June 1989. Hauling performance is all-important for commercial reasons; Foster Yeoman's target for the locomotives required that at the end of their first year in operation, each of them must have hauled a million tonnes of stone!

The GM design's exemplary haulage performance is due mainly to its electronic 'Super Series' wheel creep traction control system. This provides very accurate control of tractive effort (pulling power), giving it the ability to haul very heavy freight trains.

Nicknamed 'Leaders' by rail enthusiasts, the five GM locomotives are operated by BR traincrews and maintained at Merehead by BR engineering staff, seconded to (and supervised by) Foster Yeoman. The locomotives conform to BR standards and have many British manufactured components including seats, windscreens, buffers, couplings, wheels, AWS/DSD equipment and British automatic air brakes (the PBL system, as fitted to the Class 58).

Another link with the BR Class 58s is that the driving compartments are almost identical; even the main instrument panel follows the design of the British locomotive, but with American instruments, switches and push buttons. The overriding aim of the designers was to produce a driving compartment with the best possible environment for the driver.

Below left:
Close-up of the Class 59's cast steel bogie.

Below:
GM EMD Class 59 diesel-electric, displaying Foster Yeoman's blue and silver livery.

What the driver sees

The main illustration shows the locomotive in cutaway form. The main structural item is the heavy, deep underframe with the engine and alternator mounted low down to keep the height of the locomotive within BR's restricted loading gauge. GM's Electro-Motive Division (EMD) designs and manufactures all the major items of mechanical and electrical equipment on their locomotives, including the engine.

Inside, the Class 59 has some special features, some of which will be described here. The engine is a single EMD 645E3C series V-16 two-stroke diesel. The turbocharger is not what it seems — it is actually gear-driven by the engine via an over running clutch. At low engine revs, the exhaust gas flow is insufficient to run the turbocharger turbine alone, the mechanical drive from the engine providing most of the power.

When the engine approaches full load, however, the increased heat energy in the exhaust gas flow is enough to drive the turbine unaided; the over running clutch therefore disconnects the mechanical drive gears. Staff used to engines that produce clouds of smoke when the

Model JT26CW-55 (BR Class 59)

Wheel arrangement: Co-Co
Horsepower: 3,000 (2,238kW) at the rail
Diesel engine: Model 645E3C V-form, 16-cylinder 3,300bhp turbocharged and intercooled two-stroke
Transmission: Electric. Model AR11 MLD-D14A main alternator and rectifier powering six D77B dc series wound axle-hung traction motors
Max service speed: 60mph
Braking system: PBL-type automatic air and direct air (locomotive only)
Fuel capacity: 1,000imp gal
Max weight: 277,760lb (126 tonnes)
Length overall: 70ft (over buffers)
Height: 12ft 10in

Radiator core | Shutters | Fan & motor 1 of 2 | Lub. oil cooler | Radiator water tank | Engine speed governor | Exhaust manifold | 16 cylinder V-form 2 cycle diesel engine | Inter-cooler | Turbo-charger | Air filter | Alternators | Air compressor | Air brake equipment | Control cubicle | Power controller

David Gibbons April 1986

No.2 END | Sand box | Cast steel bogie | SAB brake unit | Traction motor 1 of 6 | Fuel tank | Fuel gauge | Battery box | Air reservoirs | Rectifier diodes | Compressor drive shaft | Parking brake module | Circuit breakers, switches & electronics

General Motors Model JT26CW-SS 3000bhp co·co diesel electric heavy freight locomotive

Fig 83

General Motors Class 59 3,300hp Co-Co diesel-electric heavy freight locomotive

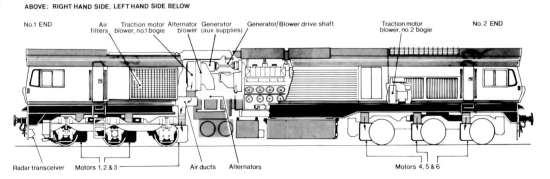

ABOVE: RIGHT HAND SIDE, LEFT HAND SIDE BELOW

No.1 END | Air filters | Traction motor blower, no.1 bogie | Alternator blower | Generator (aux. supplies) | Generator/Blower drive shaft | Traction motor blower, no.2 bogie | No.2 END

Radar transceiver | Motors 1, 2 & 3 | Air ducts | Alternators | Motors 4, 5 & 6

power controller is opened will be in for a surprise. The power unit is almost smoke-free throughout the whole range of engine outputs as a result of it being effectively turbo-supercharged!

Unlike some two-stroke engines, the GM design has four exhaust valves per cylinder, opened by twin overhead camshafts. Conventional two-stroke inlet ports are provided on the hollow cylinder liners (through which coolant is circulated), each liner being located inside an air 'box' formed in the 'V' of the engine casing above crankshaft level. This 'box' takes the place of an external combustion air manifold, and provides a degree of sound insulation. The engine is exceptionally quiet, and, like most two-strokes, revs up in a most audibly satisfying way.

The other drawing of the locomotive side shows another unusual feature. The engine drives the auxiliary alternator and the traction motor blower mechanically on a common driveshaft to which is also connected a cooling fan for the alternators, while No 2 bogie has an electrically-powered blower. In most other respects, however, the American locomotive has an interior arranged very similarly to a British one.

Making short work of 4,692 tonnes!

The Class 59's reputation for sheer hauling power – and its popularity with drivers – is well known. A single locomotive runs up from Merehead to Acton regularly with 46 102-tonne bogie hoppers in tow, a trailing load of 4,692 tonnes. The Foster Yeoman locomotive takes 28 of these wagons over the heavily-graded North London line from Acton yard to their destination at Purfleet, making short work of this 2,856-tonne load on the gradients from Acton Wells to Hampstead Heath. Only five of its eight power notches are used most of the time, the American locomotive managing to do this with around the same horsepower as a Class 58. GM's 'Super Series' wheel creep control system is partly responsible for the Class 59's performance advantage over its British counterpart.

Wheel creep is a relatively new addition to traction terminology and is used to describe the control of wheelslip, which arises when the driving wheels lose their grip altogether and spin, much like the wheels of a car trying to grip on an icy road.

On a rail traction unit, grip depends on the friction (adhesion) that exists between the wheel rim and the surface of the rail. So, by careful design of the traction motor control system, and correct driving technique, the wheels are not induced to spin by having too much power applied to them, particularly when starting from rest.

When the rails are wet or greasy, however, adhesion is lowered and wheelslip can take place very easily. In really bad conditions, with a heavy train on a steep gradient, the locomotive may slip to a standstill with the driving wheels spinning, unable to obtain a grip on the rail.

In such conditions, traction power – and tractive effort – is reduced, either automatically or by the driver, until it matches what adhesion is available. Quite apart from the time lost as a result of the train slowing down, the spinning wheels leave damaging 'wheel burns' on the rails and create problems within the overspeeding motors themselves. So, the efficiency of a traction control system and its ability to make the best use of the available adhesion under all conditions – especially unfavourable ones – is vitally important. Ultimately it influences how much the locomotive can pull which in turn effects the numbers needed to move the traffic and thus profitability.

With its 'Super Series' wheel creep system, GM has actually made a virtue of out wheelslip and turned the phenomenon to its advantage. Research into the relationship between the rail and a driven wheel showed that after a wheel begins to slip there is still a considerable amount of frictional force between the wheel and the rail. This force will increase to a peak and then decrease very sharply; therefore if the wheel is allowed to slip, or, more accurately, *creep* up to this peak – and no further – the increased friction can be used to support increased tractive effort.

Thus, the accurate control of this wheel creep is the basic principle behind the American locomotive electronic traction control system. This is able to control alternator output with great precision which in turn gives similar precise control over traction motor current and, with it, tractive effort. To work properly this relies on a parallel system of precise speed measurement. On the Class 59 a speed-sensing Doppler radar transceiver (a combined radar transmitter and receiver) obtains an independent and

Fig 85 Key

Key

1. Exhaust manifold
2. Exhaust elbow
3. Exhaust cam
4. Exhaust valve rocker arm
5. Exhaust valves (four per cylinder)
6. Fuel injector cam
7. Fuel rocker arm
8. Fuel injector
9. Air box
10. Air box cover
11. Cylinder liner
12. Piston, one of 16
13. Air inlet ports
14. Cooling water jacket
15. Cooling water inlet manifold
16. Connecting rods
17. Crankshaft
18. Crankshaft counterweight
19. Piston cooling oil manifold
20. Oil sump cover
21. Oil sump
22. Dipstick
23. Crankpin

Right:
EMD 645 series diesel engine

extremely accurate indication of groundspeed that does not depend on wheel rotation. This is compared with the current passing to the traction motors, thus giving an indication if the wheels are rotating at a speed appropriate to the indicated groundspeed. Any imbalance between the two is a measure of how much wheelslip is actually taking place.

It is easy to see that if traction motor current is automatically adjusted to correspond with that required to keep the wheels rotating within the 'controlled' slip (or creep) area this will maximise tractive effort and hence the load the locomotive can haul.

The basic elements of the GM locomotive's electric transmission are similar to the British Class 56 and 58 units, with a main traction alternator driven by the diesel engine powering dc series-wound traction motors via a rectifier. One important difference here is that the Class 59 alternator has a stator comprising two independent sets of output windings. At start-up, or during slow speed operation, when high current is demanded, the two outputs are connected in parallel to power the parallel-connected motors. This arrangement gives each motor an independent supply of current to reduce the possibility of slip.

At higher locomotive speeds when current demand is lessened and the alternator output voltage rises, the two outputs are connected together in series, this taking place automatically at 24mph.

Fig 84

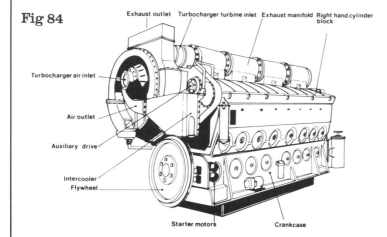

The EMD 645 series engine

The Class 59's bare engine is shown in Fig 84 minus its alternators which are mechanically coupled to, and driven from, the flywheel. Fig 85 shows a simplified outline of the powerplant in cross-section. This highlights the 'V' form of

Fig 85

Left:
EMD 645 series diesel engine cross-section

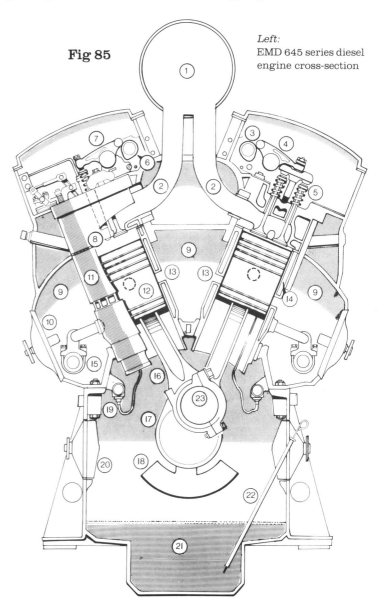

Fig 86

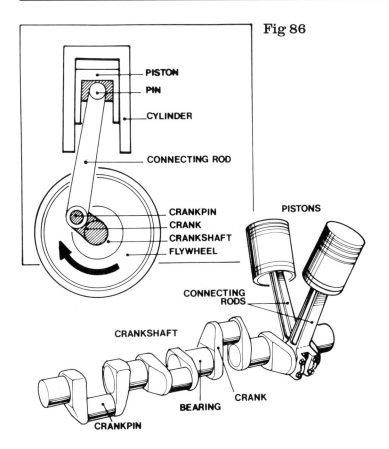

PISTON
PIN
CYLINDER
CONNECTING ROD
CRANKPIN
CRANK
CRANKSHAFT
FLYWHEEL

PISTONS
CONNECTING RODS
CRANKSHAFT
CRANK
BEARING
CRANKPIN

Fig 87   **Fig 88**   **Fig 89**   **Fig 90**

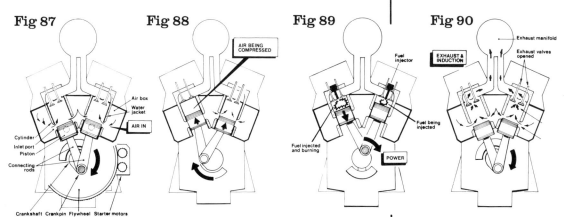

Far left:
Main crankshaft and piston components.

Above, left to right:
The two-stroke cycle.

the engine, with its cylinders arranged in two banks of eight, each pair of pistons and their connecting rods arranged to share the same crankpin on the crankshaft. Some of the features already described will be clear from the drawing. Notice the 'air box' surrounding the cylinders which channels pressure combustion air from the turbocharger to the inlet ports, and the hollow cylinder liners each containing a cooling water jacket.

The overhead camshafts, rocker-operated fuel injectors and exhaust valves, four per cylinder, can also be seen on the drawing. This EMD 645 series two-stroke engine produces 3,300bhp at 904rpm. The difference between this and the locomotive's horsepower of 3,000 is accounted for by the power needed to drive the auxiliaries, such as the various engine system pumps, the auxiliary generator and alternator/traction motor blowers.

Now that BR has discarded two-stroke diesels, readers will wonder why EMD chose this type of engine in preference to the normal four-stroke, used on most other diesels. The basic engine design was laid down before World War 2 and with 46 or more years of development it has a reputation for exceptional reliability. 'If you've got a good engine, why bother to design another' is a typical EMD comment.

How the two-stroke engine works

The secrets of BR's four-stroke engines are explained elsewhere and need not be discussed here. The main difference is that the two-stroke engine has a power stroke on every revolution of the crankshaft. Before seeing how this works, look at Fig 84 which shows the engine. Fig 85 shows a cross-section of it and Fig 86 will remind the reader of the names of the vital parts. These are basically no different from those on British four-stroke diesel engines.

The operating cycle of the EMD engine is shown in the sequence of Figs 87 to 90. In Fig 87 the engine is being started using a pair of starter motors to turn the crankshaft. This moves the pistons down, each of them uncovering an inlet port formed in the cylinder liner that allows air to enter. Next, Fig 88 shows that the rotation of the crankshaft has made the pistons start to move upwards, the piston on the left at a point where the inlet port is now closed as shown, and the air is starting to be compressed. The right-hand piston will soon do likewise. Now look at Fig 89. In the left-hand cylinder the piston will have compressed the air, it will be superheated and the injector has already sprayed oil into the cylinder so the combustion process is well under way. In the right-hand cylinder the injector has just operated.

This combustion pressure forces the pistons downwards very rapidly and with enormous force, turning the crankshaft which, through gearing and cams, opens exhaust valves in the top of the cylinder to allow the exhaust gas to escape.

As the piston moves down further (Fig 90), it uncovers the inlet port once again and more air will enter the cylinder from the air box, blown into it by a turbocharger fan. The pressurised air will also force the exhaust gas out, the flywheel – and the other pistons on their power strokes – carrying the crankshaft round. At the same time, the exhaust valves will close and the sequence will be repeated. The engine has now started and will continue to rotate as long as fuel is supplied to it. Notice on the main engine

drawing (Fig 85) that the cam used to open the fuel injector is on the left bank of cylinders (the injector for the cylinder on the right is hidden by the exhaust valves). This is mounted on the same engine-driven camshaft, so arranged and operated that it opens the valves and injectors at precisely the right time and closes them afterwards.

Thus, a power stroke occurs every half a revolution of the crankshaft; the other half of the revolution is to compress the air in readiness for the next power stroke. This much simpler operating cycle can be compared with the conventional and more complex four-stroke cycle in which four piston strokes (and two revolutions of the crankshaft) are required to complete an induction, compression, power and exhaust sequence.

Notice that the engine uses ports in the cylinder walls to get combustion air into the cylinders and valves in each cylinder head to release the exhaust gas, a process assisted by the turbo-supercharger.

The real engine produces enormous power from its 16 cylinders, each a little over 9in in diameter. Indeed, the engine is capable of producing enough electricity to keep over 2,200 one-bar electric fires going!

The turbocharger

Fig 91 shows GM's turbocharger. It has the same rotating impeller as other turbochargers, and is made to turn by an exhaust gas turbine as in normal diesel engine practice. The big difference is the overrunning clutch which also allows the engine mechanically to drive the impeller through the camshaft drive train at low engine speeds. This is because the exhaust gas flow is insufficient to power it unaided.

However, when the engine is in power notch 6, 7 or 8 the gas flow increases and is enough to drive the turbo alone, the overrunning clutch automatically disconnecting the drive gears. In this way the ingenious EMD system ensures that the engine is not robbed of power to drive the turbo at a time when maximum horsepower is required.

Power control

Fig 92 shows pictorially how the Class 59's electric power transmission system works; this was described earlier. The engine delivers a fixed amount of power for each of the

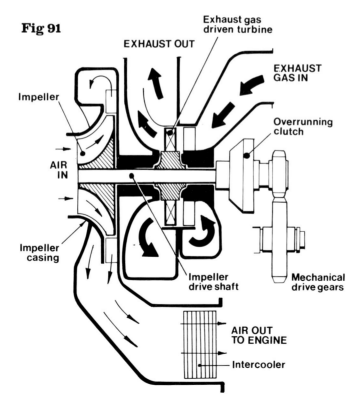

Fig 91

Exhaust gas driven turbine

EXHAUST OUT

EXHAUST GAS IN

Impeller

Overrunning clutch

AIR IN

Impeller casing

Impeller drive shaft

Mechanical drive gears

AIR OUT TO ENGINE

Intercooler

Right:
GM's turbocharger.

eight power controller notches selected by the driver. Each notch is 'sensed' by the engine governor which signals the associated load regulator, which in turn 'instructs' the control circuitry and electronics to produce an appropriate alternator output to match the horsepower of the engine. The alternator, incidentally, has a continuous rating of 7,020A.

Getting on the move

The GM design can handle exceptional loads on the move, but what happens if the locomotive is asked to start a heavy train from rest on a gradient? When the '59' is stationary, GM's 'Super Series' control system brings into play a special 'rate of change' wheelslip control system to get the locomotive started and moving up to 1.5mph. The system monitors the rate of change between the lowest motor current (indicating the fastest-turning wheelset) and the average motor current. By doing this, the system can ascertain whether the motor current — and hence tractive effort — is correct for the available rail-to-wheel friction.

The principle here is that the motors working the hardest (producing the highest tractive effort) are those accepting the highest current, so the alternator output is continuously adjusted to keep this as high as possible. The 'Super Series' wheel creep system will operate when the speed exceeds 1.5mph because it can now rely on the Doppler radar measuring true groundspeed. Wheel creep is a regime strictly controlled up to 10mph, with the slipping axle speed limited to a maximum of 14% above groundspeed. The complete system is controlled by a microcomputer, built to military specification because of the hostile environment on board a locomotive. On similar American locomotives, the computer is able to provide fault diagnosis and suggest remedies to in-service problems if required.

The circuitry also measures wheel diameter (through very small current differences between individual motors) to ensure the computed motor current takes this into account. Having a radar 'speedometer' is not a gimmick. It replaces the conventional speedometer generator (whose output is fed to an ammeter scaled in miles per hour) and thereby eliminates the possibility of a false speed reference signal caused by all the wheels slipping together.

Pulling power

GM claims that locomotives fitted with the 'Super Series' wheel creep system produce a 30% improvement in hauling capacity over conventional locomotives when the rails are slippery. With the wheel creep system in use, the driver of a Foster Yeoman locomotive can almost ignore rail conditions (unless they are exceptionally bad) and drives with the power controller kept at the chosen setting.

External noise, like wheel squealing and vibrations together with small ammeter needle deflections due to the wheels operating in the 'creep' area, will be the only evidence to the driver that the locomotive is encountering bad rail conditions. The '59' will in any case put down sand automatically if wheelslip occurs, but only enough to obtain a grip. This is to save wheel wear. The driver can still do this job himself, however, using an aptly named 'wobble stick' in place of the normal sander push button fitted to some British locomotives. It goes without saying that the wheel creep system will not operate on a dry rail.

Foster Yeoman is now operating the locomotives exclusively on its trains from Merehead on timings which are all but identical to those for similar trains that previously required two Class 56s.

Readers may like to know that EMD claims that its 645 series two-stroke engines are as fuel efficient as any four-stroke. Fuel consumption tests carried out by an American railroad operating General Electric (GE) four-stroke diesels and EMD two-stroke locomotives showed a difference of just 1% between the designs, the first test favouring the EMD two-stroke and the other naming the GE locomotive the winner. More tests followed, the result being declared a draw!

Fig 92

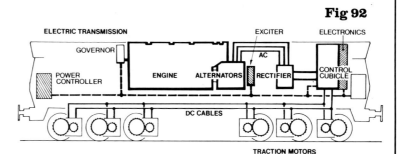

ELECTRIC TRANSMISSION EXCITER ELECTRONICS
GOVERNOR AC
POWER CONTROLLER ENGINE ALTERNATORS RECTIFIER CONTROL CUBICLE
DC CABLES
TRACTION MOTORS

Left:
Electric transmission

The New Class 60 Heavy Freight Diesel Locomotive

Introduction

Class 60 locomotive No 60001, the forerunner of a 100-strong fleet destined for Railfreight operations nationwide, is now undergoing service trials. The background to this important freight locomotive together with a description of some of its unique features is the subject of this chapter.

The heavy haul revolution

The new Class 60 diesel freight locomotive complies with a Railfreight specification written around the GM Class 59 locomotives supplied to Foster Yeoman.

These American locomotives, specially designed for heavy freight operation, regularly shift over 4,000 tonnes single-handed, and their heavy hauling ability has become legendary. The Class 59 proved that very heavy 4,000 tonne loads could be worked with a single, Co-Co (six-axle) locomotive and, to put this into perspective, a typical BR heavy (1,000 tonne) train needs two Class 37s in multiple at the head end, while for significantly heavier tonnages, a pair of Class 56 locomotives may be required on some difficult routes.

Railfreight faces severe competition from the road haulage industry for bulk transport, Railfreight's traditional marketplace. BR was convinced that it could meet this competition head-on if Class 59-style 'mega-trains', worked with a single high-performance freight locomotive, became the norm. Railfreight also needed a cost-effective replacement for some elderly locomotives, notably the Class 37 and Class 47 designs. The result was the issuing of the specification for a new heavy-haul freight design — the Class 60.

BR went out to international tender in August 1987 for the supply of 100 low-maintenance, fuel-thrifty locomotives, the order eventually going to Brush Electrical Machines which quoted an extremely short delivery period with the first unit due to be delivered only 13 months after the order was placed. Brush, to its credit, delivered on time!

Enter the Class 60

The Class 60 is a 3,100bhp diesel-electric locomotive with a number of special features. It has a maximum service speed of 60mph, weighs 126 tonnes in full working order and is powered by a single turbocharged and intercooled Mirrlees eight-cylinder in-line diesel engine, the first in-line eight to be supplied to BR since the Class 33 from the early 1960s. The powerplant is massive and very tall, its fuel injectors almost scraping the underside of the inspection hatches in the roof. Each of its eight cylinders produces nearly 400bhp with outstanding fuel economy; it has the distinction of being one of the most fuel-efficient diesel engines in the world.

Transmission is electric, with an engine-driven alternator driving dc traction motors via a rectifier. The

Above:
Class 60 bogie.

Left:
It is intended that all the Class 60s will be named. This picture shows the *Steadfast* nameplate carried by No 60001.

Above right:
Class 60 cab interior showing driving controls.

Right:
Cabside profile of the Class 60 heavy freight locomotive.

Class 60, however, differs from the ac/dc theme used on the earlier Class 56 and 58 designs and all six traction motors are separately excited and connected in parallel across the solid-state rectifier. These design improvements help to give the Class 60 exceptional hauling power, as will be seen later.

The full-width locomotive is supported on two three-axle (Co-Co) bogies. These have coil primary suspension and a secondary suspension using rubber/metal sandwich blocks to support the locomotive on its bogies.

Between the two driving compartments the locomotive is divided by partitions into three compartments; at the No 2 end there is a clean air compartment containing the electrical controls and brake equipment with the diesel engine silencer mounted externally above it. Cooling air for the alternator set is also drawn from the clean air compartment and discharged into the engine room, which forms the next compartment.

At the No 1 end is the third compartment housing the diesel engine radiators and cooling fans — all diesel locomotives are arranged with their radiators at this end — plus other equipment. The illustration shows the location of the various items of equipment familiar to the traincrew. The compartment is also the location of a crankcase extractor fan to purge the engine of unwanted fumes.

Unfiltered air for the radiators is drawn through the bodysides by two motor-driven roof-mounted 'pusher' fans, and is expelled through the roof after passing through the cooling panels. The fans are computer-controlled and temperature switches select no fan, one fan or both fans as required. The fan motors, like most of those powering auxiliary machines, are of a low maintenance ac induction type.

Fault logging and diagnostics

The control cubicle houses a comprehensive microcomputer-controlled fault logging, performance measuring and diagnostics system with its own illuminated display to show faults or malfunctions. The display can be used by the driver as an aid to fault finding. The complete system is programmable, and its scope is capable of expansion as service experience grows.

Power control system

The layout of the driving compartment and the controls is identical to the Class 58 freight locomotive. Power controls are mounted on a pedestal on the right of the driver and all the braking controls are on the left. The microcomputer-based power control system incorporates slow speed controls for MGR working plus wheel creep control, first seen on the American Class 59.

This wheel creep control system means that the Class 60 locomotive can produce around 50 tonnes of tractive effort, a record for a series production BR locomotive. Multiple working is possible, however, and in the unlikely event two locomotives are required to work together, jumper cables can be coupled, located behind an access panel below the windscreen. The panel can only be opened by maintenance staff.

Now on test

Deliveries of the first few Class 60 locomotives have started, at the time of writing, and these will leave Brush quietly to begin the testing and evaluation stage. This will include fine tuning of the system computers in response to service trials, training the depot engineering staff and giving drivers their conversion courses on the new locomotive. All the signs indicate that they will be mightily pleased with Railfreight's newest and most powerful locomotive.

Class 60 cut-away view **Fig 93**

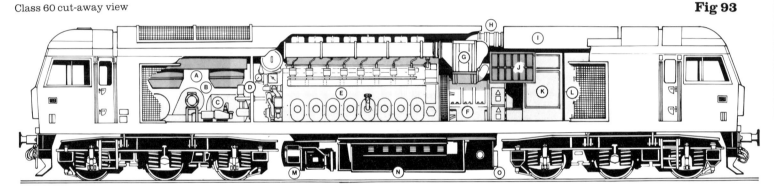

Class 60 plan view

No.1 end **Right hand (A) side**

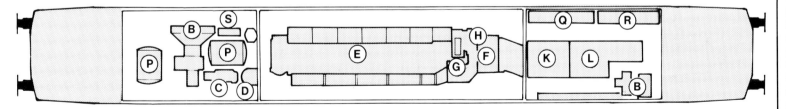

Key
A Cooling group with twin fans
B Traction motor blower
C Lubricating oil priming pumpset
D Crankcase extractor fan
E Diesel engine
F Main and auxiliary alternators
G Intercooler
H Exhaust outlet from turbocharger
I Exhaust silencer
J Engine combustion air filter
K Rectifier
L Control cubicle
M Air compressor
N Battery box
O Fuel tank
P Main air reservoirs
Q Converters and choke cubicle
R Brake equipment frame
S Fuel lift pump

Details at a glance
Wheel arrangement: Co-Co
Max service speed: 60mph
Weight: 126 tonnes
Axle load: 21.5 tonnes
Min curve: 80m
Route availability: 6
Fuel capacity: 4,500l
Diesel engine: Mirrlees-Blackstone type 8MB275T turbocharged and intercooled, producing 3,100bhp at 1,000rpm
Max tractive effort: 500kN
Main alternator: Brush BA1006A salient pole with slip rings. Self-ventilated. Continuous rating, 2,055kVA (3,164A, 375V at 1,000rpm)
Auxiliary alternator: Brush BAA702A. A six-phase 240V output excites the main alternator and the six traction motors. A three-phase 553V output, AVR controlled, powers the auxiliary machines
Traction motors: Six Brush TM2161A four pole, force ventilated with a traction motor blower for each bogie. Separately excited field windings. Continuous rating 304kW at 480rpm
Bogies: Low weight transfer design with coil spring primary suspension and rubber stack secondary suspension. All motors face inwards. Brake actuators are direct acting SAB type with no brake rigging. Two axles on each bogie have integral parking brake actuators
Brake system: Two pipe 'PBL'-type automatic air and separate straight (direct) air brake on the locomotive only

InterCity's New Mk 4 Supercoaches

Below:
The Swiss-design SIG bogie
Courtesy Metro-Cammell Ltd

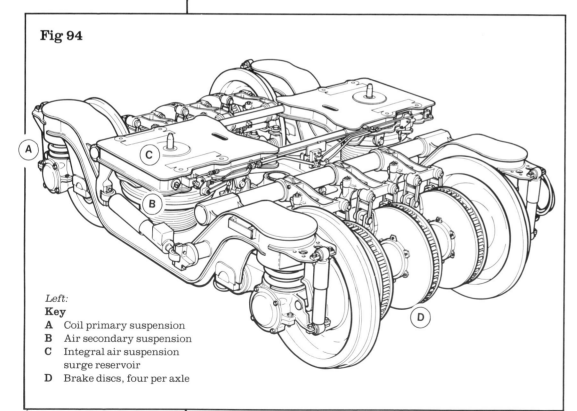

Fig 94

Left:
Key
A Coil primary suspension
B Air secondary suspension
C Integral air suspension
      surge reservoir
D Brake discs, four per axle

Introduction

The IC225 concept — BR's 140mph InterCity flagship — introduces into service the first Mk 4 passenger coaches and their driving trailers, designed to work exclusively with the Class 91 ac electric locomotives now in service. The new InterCity vehicles commenced King's Cross-Leeds workings with the start of the October 1989 timetable and will progressively take over HST workings on this route as the new coaches are delivered from the manufacturer. IC225 trains are fixed formation electric trains intended for service on the ECML between London, Leeds, Newcastle and Edinburgh, now being electrified. They are formed of nine Mk 4 vehicles marshalled between a Class 91 locomotive at one end and a Driving Van Trailer (DVT), complete with a Class 91 driving compartment and controls, at the other. Operation is on the push-pull principle with the locomotive hauling the train northbound and propelling it on its southbound journey. Though designed for 140mph, the trains will not exceed 125mph in passenger service for the time being.

The coaches

A total of 31 nine-coach trains are being supplied by Metro-Cammell Ltd, the vehicles mostly built by BREL (with a smaller number from Italian manufacturer Breda) and supplied to Metro-Cammell as bare painted shells under subcontract. All the DVT shells are sourced from BREL. There are five passenger vehicle types and all share the same Metro-Cammell-designed, integrally constructed 23m long body, carried on Swiss SIG bogies. The bogies have disc brakes with three discs per axle, primary suspension with swinging arms and coil springs, and secondary air suspension — see Fig 94. Doors are the swing plug type and power operated, a notable first for an InterCity vehicle.

All vehicles are air conditioned using energy-efficient heat pump units (as on Class 442 EMUs), and powered from Class 442-style solid-state, thyristor converter auxiliary power units fed from the BR standard single phase train supply derived from the Class 91 electric locomotive.

Standard Class cars

Three types have been built. An 'end' car fitted with retractable buffers couples to the locomotive with a drophead buckeye coupler. The opposite end has a Tightlock coupler also used between all the vehicles on the complete train. Designated TOE (Tourist Open End) by the manufacturer, it couples to the adjoining TO (Tourist Open) vehicle; both have 74 seats. The other 72-seat vehicle

(TOD) is identical to the TO/TOE but has a disabled persons' toilet and space for a wheelchair.

Pullman cars

This vehicle has a total of 46 first class reclining seats. It is marshalled between the DVT and the service vehicle.

Service vehicle

Service vehicles have a small 20-seat saloon with an adjoining kitchen and buffet bar with an arrangement similar to that on IC125 trains.

Driving Van Trailer

The DVT closely resembles a Class 91 locomotive and shares its design of driving compartment and controls. The DVT has no power equipment or traction motors. Next to the streamlined driving compartment is an entrance vestibule, a luggage area, a conductor's office and another vestibule at the train end to which passengers have access. Two sliding plug doors on each side are provided for loading purposes; eight tonnes of luggage can be carried.

Public address equipment on the conductor's desk provides keypad selectable prerecorded announcements together with automatic warning messages relayed

Below:
InterCity's Mk 4 coaches

Fig 95

Driving Van Trailer   Pullman

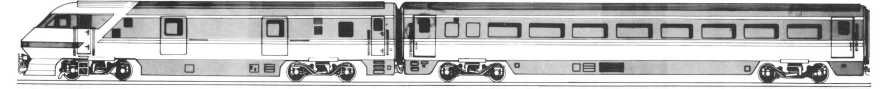

Service Vehicle   Standard

through the train if a communication handle is pulled, the driver calls, or the disabled persons' toilet alarm has been operated.

Vehicle interiors

The entrance to Mk 4 vehicles is via sliding plug doors, operated by the passengers when released by the conductor from door control panels in the vestibule at the toilet end of each car. One of the panels incorporates a PA handset and controls. These facilities allow the conductor the freedom to control the doors and to make announcements to passengers from virtually anywhere on the train.

Vestibules are larger than normal and heated. They are lit with recessed spotlights which give a welcoming glow and highlight the prominent grab handles to aid the passenger entering and leaving the vehicle. Both the floor and the walls are carpeted, a feature designed to give an impression of luxury. Two tip-up seats on standard class vehicles and one on Pullman cars in the vestibules will be appreciated by passengers on busy services. Standard class cars have two toilets, one larger than the other and fitted out with a folding table for nappy changing. The TOD, however, has a single toilet for the disabled. Pullman cars are equipped with a BT phone and one large toilet. All the toilet facilities are to a high standard with attractive fittings and with easy-clean materials and surfaces.

Sliding vestibule doors are power operated like their Mk 3 counterparts but with touch button operation. These lead into quite the most attractive interiors yet seen on a BR vehicle. Pullman cars have a 2+1 seating arrangement in which the aisle changes from one side of the vehicle to the other in the middle of the car to provide a central area for a catering trolley, or simply to allow passengers to pass safely.

Colour is in grey tones, black and chrome in first class saloons with this scheme being continued in standard class vehicles but warmed with touches of red. First class seats are similar to those on refurbished Mk 3 vehicles; those in standard class saloons have the backrest cut back at head level to heighten the impression of space. All vehicles have smoked glass partitions from floor to ceiling to lessen the 'aircraft interior' effect. This has been beautifully (and skilfully) done in the first class saloons to partition the seating in a subtle way, encouraging groups to keep together.

The power-operated entrance doors are speed sensed to prevent them from opening when the train is moving. Door control signals are carried through the train using a frequency division multiplex (FDM) system. These signals, and the TDM remote control signals between the locomotive and the DVT, use special UIC cables, connections and sockets to provide a high quality transmission line.

Below:
The tastefully-appointed Mk 4 Pullman interior.